D1193911

Many Missions

The 180-acre Research Triangle Institute campus is in the center of North Carolina's Research Triangle Park. This aerial photograph was made in the fall of 1990.

Many Missions

Research Triangle Institute's First 31 Years

by Charles X. Larrabee

Research Triangle Institute
Research Triangle Park, North Carolina

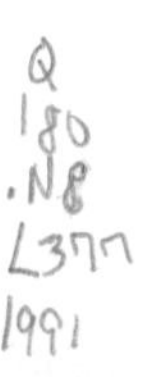
Q
180
.N8
L377
1991

Contents

Preface

This account of Research Triangle Institute's first 31 years contains too few names of individual researchers and too few adjectives to describe even those few.

The omission of names is regrettable, for legions of men and women have made crucial contributions to RTI's success. The roll call would be impossibly long, however, and decisions about whom to include/exclude would be at least presumptuous.

As for the missing adjectives, two are particularly noticeable: brilliant and dedicated. Readers may insert them at will.

A history, even a corporate history, at least one of any value, can't be written by committee and shouldn't have to be subjected to layers of review and approval. This one hasn't been. Its tone, choices, and perspectives are solely those of the author, who was an Institute staff member when it was written and whose point of view is three cheers for RTI. George R. Herbert corrected some errors of fact and straightened out a handful of issues and events that the author miscalled. He is the ultimate authority on every aspect of RTI's purposes, policies, intentions, and effects. George L. Simpson, Jr., clarified matters pertaining to the founding days. Reid Maness, RTI communications manager, edited later technical passages with beneficial effect. These three and others suggested improvements, some of which were made, some not.

The notes and correspondence of Simpson, George Watts Hill, and Herbert are beyond price as sources for an understanding of RTI's place and function within the Research Triangle. The author has had ready access to them. Elizabeth J. Aycock and Pearson H. Stewart mined nuggets from their memories.

Their recall and their Research Triangle Foundation files, along with those of Archie K. Davis and Ned E. Huffman, will have to be the basis for a Research Triangle Park history. The one you are reading is about the Research Triangle Institute.

Until now, only the sketchiest accounts of the Research Triangle's formative years have been published. Standing alone on events leading to December 29, 1958, and both cited in context, have been Duke University Professor W. B. Hamilton's monograph that appeared in the spring 1966 issue of *The*

South Atlantic Quarterly, and Mary Virginia Currie Jones's 1978 thesis devoted to Romeo H. Guest, whose official Research Triangle involvement ended in October 1959. Versions of early concept and growth are also included in a 1967 booklet issued by Louis R. Wilson of Chapel Hill. A chapter in Harvard Professor Ezra F. Vogel's book *Comeback*, published in 1985 by Simon and Schuster, is excellent. Both he and Hamilton report on the total Research Triangle program up to their dates of publication, giving appropriate notice to RTI's role.

For the rest, most magazine and newspaper articles about how the Research Triangle Park and Research Triangle Institute started, and how they grew, are glittering generalities, numerous and indeed welcome, but only marginally helpful for this narrative. (Many local, state, and national writers have produced fine science stories about RTI research.) By far the best of the overall Research Triangle reporting are Robert W. McDowell's in the June 1981 issue of *We the People of North Carolina*, and Luther J. Carter's in *Science* for November 12, 1965, and June 30, 1978. Also of interest are a section in the Greenwood Press's 1982 *Research Institutions and Learned Societies*, and an article by UNC Professor William F. Little in the November 1988 issue of *The World and I*.

Specific to RTI, authoritative sources are Board of Governors minute books, Herbert's reports at board meetings and his notes for talks at the annual luncheons honoring staff members upon completion of ten years at RTI, the Institute's *Hypotenuse* magazine from September 1964, the *RTItems* staff newsletter from May 1978, summary and capability publications and, beginning in 1984, annual reports. Finally, a resource of inestimable worth is Carolyn Hope Harris, RTI's assistant corporate secretary. Without the assurance of her patience and help, as well as Herbert's, this document wouldn't have been attempted.

Charles X. Larrabee
RTI Corporate Staff 1964-1990

September 1990

Introduction

It was the turning of another page more than the end of an era when George Herbert stepped aside at the end of September 1989 after 31 years as Research Triangle Institute's founding president.

During those years many, many pages turned at RTI, but the Institute was far too busy with today's problems, tomorrow's pressures, and next week's opportunities to notice anything so indistinct as an era. It was in existence all along, of course, but the dimensions and definitions of a "Herbert era" will have to await historians of another generation. There isn't anything to compare it with yet.

On Monday morning October 2, 1989, Tom Wooten arrived at work to take the reins of a sizeable and thriving research institute marked by professional excellence, uncompromising ethical standards, and fiscal integrity. These qualities endure.

Thanks to an exceptional staff and reputation, RTI is positioned to continue and expand its already substantial contributions to the quality of life and to scientific advance. It is an enviable inheritance. But the best parts of the Institute's history lie ahead, as they always have.

The following pages are, however, about RTI's past, from the end of 1958 to the end of 1989. They are not an exact chronology; neither do they come within miles of imparting the extraordinary variety and quality of the Institute's scientific undertakings. But they do try to relate the order and the essence of RTI's inception, establishment, and performance. It's a remarkable story. This is one way to tell it.

1. Project #1, With Some Befores and Some Afters

The idea was exhilarating, bewitching, even audacious. The half-million-dollar start-up grant from privately contributed funds was sufficient, even generous at that time and place. The level of university participation and support was unique, and remains so.

Yet when Research Triangle Institute began project operations on March 2, 1959, its chief research asset was staff. Staff has always been RTI's chief research asset and will be for as long as the Institute exists. The caliber of RTI's scientific and support professionals is the substance of the reputation for excellence and ethics that RTI has earned, and maintained, throughout its more than 30 years.

Gertrude M. Cox embodied that reputation. Long acclaimed within the world's statistical sciences community, and beyond question its First Lady, Cox's early commitment to RTI was, along with that of Alva L. Finkner, an endorsement of vital import to the Research Triangle Institute. RTI was by no means a tentative enterprise, ever, but at that time it was untested, untried, and virtually unknown. Cox was none of the above.

Although she and Finkner were the first scientists pledged to RTI, they weren't the first researchers on its payroll. That distinction goes to survey statistician John Monroe, survey specialists Charles V. Mercer and Nancy R. Campbell, and secretary Charline B. Hardison. These four constituted RTI's Statistics Research Division.

On Monday, March 2, 1959, Monroe, Mercer, and Hardison showed up for work as usual at the offices of the Institute of Statistics' Survey Operations Unit at the University of North Carolina (UNC) in Chapel Hill. Their responsibilities were unchanged from the previous Friday. Their employer, however, was no longer the state university, but the Research Triangle Institute.

Campbell's circumstances were similar, with the difference that she was in Nashville, Tennessee, where she had been for more than two months overseeing data collection for an Institute of Statistics family health survey that became, on March 2, RTI's first project.

Years later she'd recall that "I didn't even see RTI until I'd been on the payroll a couple of weeks. It occupied the whole second floor of the Home Security Life Building in Durham. John and Charles and Charline hadn't moved over yet from Chapel Hill, and all that was there was an office for George and an office for Bill. The rest was empty space and a lot of partitions, but I knew I was in the right place because in the middle of the floor there was a big crate labeled 'Nancy's desk.' When I saw it I almost went back to Nashville."

She refers to George R. Herbert and William H. Perkins, Jr., who preceded the four university staff members on RTI's employee roster. Herbert had become president of the still unincorporated Institute on December 1, 1958, and Perkins came aboard on February 9 to keep him company.

Both had been employed in New York at the American and Foreign Power Company, Herbert as treasurer, Perkins as a corporate accountant. During the next 30 years Perkins, unlike Herbert, enjoyed a series of RTI promotions, including election as treasurer in 1968 and in 1977 as vice president.

Along with the Monroes*, Mercer, Hardison, the Nashville survey, and Cox and Finkner on a part-time basis beginning April 1, RTI also inherited several Institute of Statistics research proposals and two other projects, both with March 2 starting dates. One was to assess the feasibility of a North Carolina State College evaluation of the 1959 census of agriculture. It led, in turn, to project #7, in which RTI conducted the evaluation in the southeastern region for the U.S. Department of Commerce. The other project, for the U.S. Department of Agriculture, was a 10-county survey of North Carolina farmers who were just then becoming eligible for Old Age Survivors Disability and Health Insurance benefits.

In contrast with the whirlwind multiplicity of disciplines and subjects that mark RTI's later years, all but two of the first 20 research contracts were in statistics. Both exceptions will be dealt with in a little while and both were landmarks of 1959, a year in which a very great deal was happening all at once.

Project #1's antecedents went back 15 years, to 1944. It was then that Cox, who was the first woman to become a full professor and department head at N.C. State and the first person anywhere in the country to head a university department of statistics, had founded the Institute of Statistics. Originally on campus in Raleigh, it expanded two years later to include Chapel Hill when a Department of Mathematical Statistics was organized there. In 1949 Cox played a major role in establishing the Department of Biostatistics, also in Chapel Hill.

* Nancy Campbell and John Monroe, both of whom had left RTI by then, were married in 1962. They returned to North Carolina in 1968 from the Washington, D.C., area, where John was a Public Health Service statistician and Nancy a statistical assistant in the Bureau of the Census. She rejoined RTI that same year, and remained for 22 years as a senior survey specialist.

(For these and later achievements, Cox received the O. Max Gardner Award, which is the state university system's highest, and the Watauga Medal, N.C. State's highest nonacademic recognition. In 1970 she attended the dedication of Gertrude Cox Hall, a seven-story research building at N.C. State. In 1975 Cox was elected to the National Academy of Sciences, one of what were then 21 women members. She died at age 78 in 1978.)

In 1954 Cox created the Survey Operations Unit (SOU) at Chapel Hill to provide southeastern educational, governmental, and private agencies with a facility for testing the results of research in sampling theory and methodology. It was activated by a $24,000 grant from the Institute of Statistics and quickly became self-supporting. At Cox's invitation, UNC's Institute for Research in the Social Sciences became a joint sponsor of SOU to benefit more individuals and groups within the university whose research called for reliable survey data.

Enjoining the reader to keep in mind SOU's strong intercampus affiliations and the quality of its performance for faculty and departments at both UNC and N.C. State, the order of events in RTI's story must drop back very briefly to the Research Triangle Committee, Inc., to its Working Committee, and to the Research Institute Committee.

The Research Triangle Committee, Inc., was created on September 25, 1956. Chapter 9 discusses its inception, formation, membership, and actions. The RTC's chairman was Robert M. Hanes of Winston-Salem, chairman of the Wachovia Bank. Its executive director was George L. Simpson, Jr., a UNC sociology professor on leave. He took the job on October 1.

The RTC was complemented by a Working Committee of three officials from each of the three Triangle universities—UNC, State, and Duke University in Durham. One official (the others are named in Chapter 9) was D. W. Colvard, dean of the School of Agriculture at N.C. State and the person to whom Gertrude Cox nominally reported.

Simpson recalls that a contract research institute at an unspecified location somewhere along the chord of the Research Triangle rainbow was "always in the air." The idea was probably raised as much as two years earlier by Paul M. Gross, vice president of Duke University, and he presented it formally at the Governor's Mansion in February 1955. A renowned chemist, Gross was perhaps the south's most prominent scientist. Decorated with the Medal of Merit by President Truman, president of the American Association for the Advancement of Science, an initial member and vice chairman of the National Science Foundation, and a founder of the Oak Ridge Associated Universities, he was respected by industry, government, and academia alike, moving easily in the top echelon of American science policy.

On January 18, 1957, Hanes appointed a Research Institute Committee. Its chairman was Brandon P. Hodges (no relation to Governor Luther H. Hodges), an executive of the Champion Paper and Fibre Company in Canton, N.C., and a former state treasurer. Members were Robert T. Armstrong, a Charlotte-based vice president of the Celanese Corporation of America; Paul Gross; J. Harold Lampe, dean of engineering at N.C. State; C. W. "Chick" Reynolds, assistant works manager for the Western Electric Company in Winston-Salem, the state's major employer of electrical engineers; and William M. Whyburn, the Consolidated University of North Carolina's vice president for research and graduate studies.

Simpson was this committee's executive also. After only ten months, chairman Brandon Hodges died late in 1957. As his successor, Hanes and Gov. Hodges agreed on George Watts Hill, board chairman of the Durham Bank & Trust Company, now Central Carolina Bank.

The committee's charge was to determine if a contract research institute was feasible. If so, how should it be organized and operated? How much would it cost to get started? Who should run it? What should it do? Where would it fit in a Research Triangle that was, as yet, shapeless in all but name?

A confident "Yes" was the answer to the feasibility question. Hill's committee and Simpson found solid, although necessarily tentative, encouragement from meetings and correspondence with existing research institutes, with research executives and scientists in the major university-research-industry centers of the San Francisco Bay Area, Boston-Cambridge, Princeton, Los Angeles, and from already hopeful North Carolina businessmen and university faculties. Some of the latter, recruited by Simpson as ambassadors for overall Research Triangle promotion, returned from their travels to report positive reactions.

Especially active in ambassadorial endeavors were UNC's William F. Little for chemistry, Kenneth E. Penrod of Duke for pharmaceuticals, N.C. State's William D. Stevenson for electronics, John F. Lee of State for engineering, James S. Bethel of State and Leon E. Chaikin of Duke for forestry, and William A. Newell of State for textiles.

Armed with literature advertising the Research Triangle's university research resources, its abundance of trained and experienced professionals, and the area's cultural attractions and pleasant living environment, they and others within two years had called on peers, colleagues, and prospects at 211 industrial and federal research establishments. The travelers were handicapped by the lack of anything to sell, or to make proposals about; their embassy was to spread the word that something worth attention was going on in North Carolina.

Even the Soviet Union chipped in to supplement efforts by the Research Triangle committees and the novel band of faculty salesmen. The successful launch and orbiting of the Sputnik satellite in October 1957 shocked the American public into overdue recognition of the nation's lagging scientific resources. Although hardly specific to the Research Triangle's purposes, Sputnik spurred significant increases in U.S. scientific education expenditures, in the supply of research and engineering manpower, and in opportunities for technology-based industrial expansion. Its effects on the Research Triangle's fortunes were tangential at best, but relevant nevertheless.

In May 1957 the institute committee reported agreement on several general principles. In Simpson's summary they were that: (1) a research institute in the Research Triangle is both feasible and desirable; (2) the three universities may properly cooperate with it; (3) it should be at a high scientific level to carry out fundamental as well as applied research as a means for encouraging faculty participation; and (4) it will require no financial support from the universities.

By early 1958 the institute committee clearly recognized its need for a concrete starting point, some proposal for research work that would be at a high level, that could begin in minimum time and at reasonable cost, and that would offer the prospect of profitable contracts.

To Dean Colvard, whose given name and academic title were the same, Cox and her Institute of Statistics filled the bill. He pressed Simpson to approach her. She signaled her willingness. With the expectation of a research institute affirmed by Hill's and Hanes' committees, Simpson and Cox agreed that she would seek the concrete starting place by retooling elements of the Institute of Statistics to meet new, undefined specifications.

The Research Triangle Committee, Inc., the Working Committee, and the Research Institute Committee all spent months exploring territory they hadn't previously known was there. Now it was Cox's turn at the clean blackboard.

The scope and method of the entire institute would rest with Hill's committee and Simpson. Cox would concentrate on the first operating unit. She and Simpson tentatively called it Research Planning and Evaluation, but they meant statistics research. N.C. State chancellor Carey H. Bostian and Consolidated University president William C. Friday backed them. A "Dear Dad" letter from Watts Hill to John Sprunt Hill brought the university a mid-February 1958 gift of Wachovia Bank stock valued at $16,000. With expense funds in hand, Friday authorized Cox to proceed with sketching the broad outline and many particulars of the first component of a scientific institution that had no name, no staff, no money, an optimistic but vague mission, and a small, enthusiastic cheering section.

Cox went right to work, enlisting Institute of Statistics faculty for service on what she dubbed the Committee of 7. In addition to herself, its members were: Richard L. Anderson, mathematical statistics; Al Finkner, experimental statistics; Henry L. "Curly" Lucas, animal sciences and statistics; David D. Mason, plant sciences and statistics; Robert J. Monroe, chemistry and statistics; and Henry F. "Cotton" Robinson, plant genetics and statistics.

Referring to these varied professional specialties, Finkner has identified as a standard part of Cox's doctrine that statistics research does not exist for its own sake alone, but finds greater worth in serving the social goals and technical needs of other substantive fields. This principle endures at the almost impossibly multifaceted RTI today in the "single institute" concept that has at times been regarded with some indifference but that steadily gains greater honor in the observance than in the breach. More about this later.

The paramount benefits to RTI from the Committee of 7 were Cox and Finkner. For more than six months both of them gave the committee nearly full time, becoming enmeshed in and finally captivated by Institute planning and prospects. It is fruitless to try to imagine what RTI would have become without these two, especially, in the long run, Finkner. But there had to be a Cox first.

From the perspective of 31 years, too much of the 7's time and effort went into emphasizing basic research as the primary mode of operation, into particularizing the conditions for joint RTI/university appointments, into salary scales and hourly wage rates, into organization charts and job descriptions. Indeed, the committee's deliberations have their greatest interest today for those matters in which they went astray.

For example, one committee memorandum was miles off base in its speculation that "A permanent staff of four to six statisticians . . . may eventually be required." Thirty years may or may not be eventually, but at the end of 1988 RTI's full-time staff included 31 men and women with Ph.D.s in statistics and another 69 holding the master's degree, an even one hundred and going up.

Another bad guess, but one based on good precedent, concerned statistical research for industry. At State College and through the two-campus Institute of Statistics, Cox had encouraged and built extensive faculty consulting relationships with large and small corporations, as well as with government agencies. In addition to U.S. civil and military departments, United Nations organizations, and foundations, the list of Consolidated University statistical and survey research clients included, along with smaller companies, two dozen from what was then the new Fortune 500 ranking.

This record led the Committee of 7 to the conjecture that it would "be possible to obtain many research contracts immediately with various industries, each of which would return $50,000 to $60,000 annually." It was an overstatement. Experts consulting with industry for a day or two per month is one thing; the successful marketing of longer-term research contracts proved to be quite another.

The first commercial contract in RTI's Statistics Research Division wasn't signed until February 1960.* It was a small ($1,138) feasibility study for Union Carbide Nuclear that was promptly followed by a $10,000 project, completed the same year, to optimize the company's drilling patterns for its uranium explorations in Colorado. Work began on two large commercial contracts during 1961. One was a two-year project in statistical reliability for Bell Telephone Laboratories (a former Cox client) for what was then, to RTI at least, the whopping contract amount of $170,897. The other, valued at $332,300 over seven years, was a Union Carbide Chemicals study of statistical methods for chemical experimentation. During RTI's first six years the Statistics Research Division had only 11 other commercial contracts, one for $100,000 with Sears, Roebuck and another for $59,300 with United Fruit, but the rest much smaller, often in the under-$5,000 range. The division was, however, busily occupied with government clients.

A not-so-incidental final fact about project #1 is that the client was the National Air Pollution Control Administration, which was one of the U.S. Public Health Service units that were combined in 1970 to form the Environmental Protection Agency. In terms of cumulative dollar volume over the years, the EPA has been RTI's second largest client, topped only by the U.S. Department of Health and Human Services. Together, DHHS and the EPA have consistently accounted for half or more of RTI's annual contract revenue.

* A study on missile reliability had been completed in October of the previous year for Bell Telephone Laboratories through a $4,000 subcontract from the Institute of Statistics.

2. Setting the Stage: I. The Founding Universities

For the Research Triangle Institute, its founding universities are everything: initiators, incorporators, owners, governors, colleagues, partners, and friends; the works.

George Simpson, one of our story's heroes, came very close in 1978 when he recalled that "There was never a time when RTI was not an integral part, the central part, of the Research Triangle concept." Yet the concept itself, and the Research Triangle's very name, arose from the geographic accident that places three major research universities in neighboring communities—the University of North Carolina in Chapel Hill, Duke University in Durham, and North Carolina State University in Raleigh. The resources of education, scientific research, and professionally trained men and women that the schools represent are the alpha and omega of the whole Research Triangle proposition.

Writing to faculty members and administrators at the three campuses in 1965, Duke chemistry professor Marcus E. Hobbs, another hero, stated that "From the time of RTI's inception, it was recognized that the presence of the universities here in the Triangle area would be the Institute's greatest asset. It was acknowledged then, and has been confirmed with each passing year, that an organization such as RTI could exist and grow here only as it drew upon and benefited from university resources. With the growth of the Institute's staff, it has become an important component of the Triangle community, and the mutually rewarding association of RTI staff and the universities' faculties, anticipated when the Institute was founded, is well under way."

A quarter of a century later the association is firmly in place, and prospering.

University Governance of RTI

RTI management reports to a Board of Governors that represents the university, business, and professional communities, and to an Executive Committee elected by the board. The full board meets twice annually, the Executive Committee eight times, and both of them on call of their respective chairmen.

George Watts Hill was elected chairman of the board at its second meeting, convened in Raleigh's Sir Walter Hotel at 11:15 a.m. on January 9, 1959. He retains the title and the responsibilities that go with it. (The board's first meeting was at ten o'clock that same morning in the same place. Governor Luther H. Hodges was its chairman and served in that capacity for an hour and a quarter.) On July 28, 1989, the board created the new post of vice chairman, electing George Herbert to fill it effective October first.

Simpson served as Executive Committee chairman from January 9, 1959, until August 31, 1962, when Hobbs succeeded him. Upon becoming provost of Duke University, Hobbs resigned the position in January of 1969, and in February UNC Chemistry Department chairman William F. Little was elected to succeed him. In December of 1977 Little, who was by then UNC vice provost for development and public service, resigned from the chairmanship but remained on the committee, and Hobbs once again assumed this position of key significance to RTI's development.

RTI by-laws authorize a Board of Governors of up to 32 members, including three—Hill, Friday, and Herbert—whom the by-laws specify by name. The late Paul Gross was also specified as a permanent member.

Five governors hold seats on the board by virtue of their positions. They are the president of The University of North Carolina, the president of Duke University, the chancellor of the University of North Carolina at Chapel Hill, the chancellor of North Carolina State University, and the president of Research Triangle Institute.

Nine board members are appointed from the universities, one by the president of The University of North Carolina, two by the chancellor of N.C. State, two by the chancellor of UNC-Chapel Hill, and four by the president of Duke.

Up to 15 other governors are elected annually from the national business and professional communities by the Members of the Corporation.

Members of the Corporation fulfill the role of RTI shareholders by their annual election of these governors. There are nine of them, including Lifetime Member George Watts Hill. Four are the chairmen and presidents of The University of North Carolina and of Duke University. Four others are elected, two from and by the Duke University board of trustees, and two from and by the board of governors of The University of North Carolina.

A separate category of Lifetime Governor recognizes retired board members who made extraordinary contributions to the progress and welfare of RTI. They have been Robert T. Armstrong, the late Frank A. Daniels, Sr., the late Grover M. Hermann, the late Walter J. Peterson, and the late W. Bailey Sellars. The names, affiliations, and terms of all past and present governors are listed in Appendix III.

University Nomenclature

Two of the three Research Triangle universities and their governing institution have experienced name changes during RTI's years.

In 1958 the state's Consolidated University had one president, whose office was in Chapel Hill, and a chancellor at each of three campuses: the University of North Carolina, located in Chapel Hill; North Carolina State College, located in Raleigh; and the Women's College, located in Greensboro and not involved with RTI's formation and governance.

Major legislation in 1972 created a state university system, with its president still in Chapel Hill, of 16 constituent institutions, each with its own chancellor. The Consolidated University, or General Administration, was transformed into The (with a capital T) University of North Carolina. The Raleigh campus was by then N.C. State University and retained this designation, and the name of the other Triangle institution became the University of North Carolina at Chapel Hill.

These pages use variations that shouldn't be hard to follow. State College, N.C. State, N.C. State University, and NCSU all refer to Raleigh. UNC-Chapel Hill, Carolina, UNC-CH and, except where the capital T is clearly implied, UNC all mean Chapel Hill. Consolidated University, General Administration, The University of North Carolina, and state university system are synonymous here.

In 1924 Trinity College in Durham became Duke University, and Duke University it remains.

University/RTI Relationships

If involvement in designing and launching the Research Triangle concept wasn't the first example of cooperation between Duke and the two principal campuses of the state university, it has proved to be the most innovative, the most transforming, the most significant, and the most enduring. According to William Friday, president of the Consolidated University for 30 years from 1956 to 1986, "There was no history of the three universities cooperating on the scale it would require for the Research Triangle Park to succeed." Other quotations by him on this topic will appear later.

Nothing like this three-university teaming ever happened in America before, nor has it since. The results are now spread over three counties for all the world to see. During three decades, the world has come in a steady stream for an envious look at North Carolina's university-based Research Triangle.

A chronicle targeted specifically on RTI isn't the place to even attempt a catalog of the state, regional, and university benefits that accrue from the development of the Research Triangle Park and the Institute. For the universities alone, a partial list of the consequences that accompany RTPark growth might include enlarged endowment, construction, and equipment funding; internship and training grants; almost exponential increases in employment opportunities for graduates; a large and diverse pool of talent from which to make adjunct research and teaching appointments; access to specialized facilities; cooperative research with federal agency and corporate sponsors; a reservoir of supplementary scientific resources that aid in recruiting graduate students and distinguished faculty.

For RTI, "pervasive" is the one word best suited to describe the relationships with its parent universities. They begin with governance; they affect, for the better, virtually all aspects of RTI research endeavor. Examples will appear in context.

Givens are the academic environment and associations that contribute both professionally and socially to productive research. Within that environment, resources abound which RTI couldn't dream of duplicating on its own.

The availability of expert assistance from faculty consultants located no farther away than the corners of the Triangle can be a decisive factor in winning competitive research contracts. Often enough—as in chemistry, engineering, and epidemiology, in policy and economic studies, statistics research, and social science surveys—RTI contracts and university grants provide for a portion of the work to be carried out at one or more of the universities and a portion within RTI. The converging interests of RTI staff and university faculty have been evident in many collaborations, notable among them mass spectrometry, semiconductors and, between Duke Medical Center surgeons and RTI electrical engineers, speech processing strategies to improve the performance of cochlear implants in stimulating the auditory nerves of patients who have severe hearing impairments.

Joint and adjunct faculty appointments allow RTI scientists to teach, supervise graduate study, and coauthor papers and books with their university counterparts. Space and equipment are often shared, and in late 1966 RTI accelerated its building program to accommodate a UNC laboratory. RTI routinely draws upon university library collections. RTI staff members at all levels enroll in university course work, in many instances for undergraduate and graduate degrees, and participate in any number of seminars, colloquiums, lecture series, and informal technical gatherings. They do not, however, benefit from preferential consideration for basketball tickets or for campus parking stickers.

3. PROPOSAL #1

By the end of 1958, as related in Chapter 9, Research Triangle Committee fund-raising had been successfully completed, George Herbert had been hired as RTI president, and decisions were made that Cox would transfer to RTI from State College and her Survey Operations Unit from UNC-Chapel Hill. Accomplishments were beginning to catch up with hopes.

Even earlier, an opportunity to submit to the Atomic Energy Commission a proposal for establishing a regional isotope development laboratory gave strong indications that the long-planned Research Triangle Institute was on the verge of becoming a real Research Triangle Institute.

The action date for this transformation was dictated by AEC requirements that a formal, written proposal must come from a legally constituted entity, and that the document must be mailed in time to bear a 1958 postmark.

This deadline led to the filing of RTI's articles of incorporation on Friday, December 29, the last working day of the year. They were logged in by the N.C. Secretary of State's office at 11:41 a.m. (Eight minutes earlier, an amendment to the Research Triangle Committee's articles, in force since 1956, changed the committee's name to Research Triangle Foundation.) After lunch, at Herbert's request, Committee/Foundation planning expert Pearson H. Stewart took the proposal to the post office.

"In the beginning, there was Buck," Herbert has written to and about Arthur C. Menius, Jr. In 1958 Buck Menius was head of the Physics Department at N.C. State College in Raleigh. He'd had a long scientific association with the Atomic Energy Commission and among his friends there was Paul C. Aebersold, director of the AEC's Office of Isotopes Development. Menius knew of the AEC's interest in creating radioisotope applications centers to serve industry, and was aware that plans were nearing completion to establish them at the University of Chicago, MIT, and Georgia Tech.

So, with Aebersold's encouragement, he proposed a North Carolina location. Typical of the spirit of generosity that was and remains such a striking feature of the whole Research Triangle enterprise, he promoted not his own institution and department, but RTI which, as yet, were initials that appeared only in memorandums and committee minutes.

Aebersold welcomed the notion. Menius and RTCommittee executive director George Simpson met with him in Washington, D.C., on October 8,

1958. At that meeting Aebersold orally committed $160,000. It is probable that he and others at the AEC were not unaware that U.S. Rep. Carl Durham, a Chapel Hill resident, was chairman of the Joint Congressional Committee on Atomic Energy and unlikely to look with disfavor on the funding of one of the new AEC centers within his district. (In later years, redistricting placed Chapel Hill and the RTPark in separate districts.)

Menius became the principal author of that first, and successful, RTI proposal. Herbert, who officially came aboard on December 1, helped with commas and with passages describing the Research Triangle concept and RTI's function. Under date of January 1959, which appears on the proposal's title page, he could accurately assert that RTI was officially in being, and that its first research unit was "in the area of statistics . . . . under the direction of Miss Gertrude Cox." Cox's name went on RTI's personnel roster January 2, 1959, although she and Finkner weren't entered on the payroll until April 1, both of them on a part-time basis to begin with.

The proposal that Menius produced was, unsurprisingly, both informed and persuasive. Its claims for the proposing institution were necessarily modest, but its technical portions were notable. Differing from the many oral and written expressions of mutual interest among individuals at the three universities, and from statements of their common purpose contained in correspondence and promotional literature, Menius's proposal was the first technical document to set forth, for a potential client's consideration, the advantages of the Triangle's multi-institutional resources.

Its catalog of radioisotope-related facilities, staff, and experience referenced professional schools and graduate departments at all three campuses. It reported, too, that many of them were already performing valuable services for industry and governments through grants and contractual research.

And it sounded a leitmotif that was to ring again and again throughout the next thirty years: "These three institutions can offer what one institution finds most difficult—the engineering and industrial knowledge supported by research and advanced concepts nurtured in an academic atmosphere. . . [B]asic research and practical engineering, tempered by a close cooperation in a small geographic area, afford a cogent reason for the location of industry and research in this region."

Addressing the larger theme of economic development, Menius noted "the fervor in the south for industrial expansion," North Carolina's pioneering efforts in this regard, and the state's "environment of healthy progress [in which] new techniques and methods find their most enthusiastic reception."

Proposal #1 was also specifically responsive, as it had to be, to the Atomic Energy Commission's objectives, which were to promote industry awareness of the savings to be realized from radioisotopes and radiation in solving industrial problems.

At a Raleigh news conference on March 24, 1959, Aebersold and the AEC's Oscar M. Bizzell joined Herbert in announcing the signing of a $160,000 agreement to establish an Isotopes Development Laboratory at RTI. The master contract eventually reached a total amount of $980,704 through May of 1969.

Following the news conference, a jubilant Gov. Hodges told a luncheon gathering that it was "wonderful news of immediate significance and thrilling future potential." He was right on both counts.

More than a month earlier, upon notification of the contract award, Herbert had begun recruiting a laboratory director.

Ralph L. Ely, Jr., first saw RTI early in February 1959. He was then employed in Pittsburgh as technical vice president of an engineering firm engaged in research and product development for the AEC and segments of the nuclear power industry.

He had already resolved to resign this position, a decision known to Aebersold and others at the AEC. They promptly called him to Herbert's attention, and a telephone call brought him and his wife to the Raleigh-Durham Airport.

Clad in the woollies that shielded them from Pittsburgh's snow and icy blasts, they descended from their plane into a mild and sunny afternoon, the Triangle area at its deep-winter best. Eleanor Ely was sold on the spot. Ely himself met with the RTI staff (it didn't take long, just Herbert and Perkins), visited Hodges and Simpson, and toured the campuses to talk with university scientists, particularly fellow physicist Menius and his colleagues at N.C. State.

Of entrepreneurial bent and lively, eclectic interests, Ely knew a great idea and a bracing challenge when he saw them. Like others to follow he jumped at the chance to take part, giving scant attention to incidentals such as fringe benefits or degree of job security. He was Herbert's first long-lasting scientific recruiting success* and agreed to report for work on May 7.

By the time he arrived, RTI had commissioned and leased a structure at 807 Bacon Street, Durham, in what was called DIDCo Park, short for Durham Industrial Development Corporation. Known to RTI as the Bacon Street Annex, it was a 10,000-square-foot shell, later enlarged to 13,000 square feet,

* Ely himself had a recruiting contact of lasting significance for RTI. Sitting with a young woman and her baby during an airplane trip, he learned that her husband was an N.C. State engineering graduate whose job was in Florida but whose heart was in North Carolina. Upon deplaning, Ely met James B. Tommerdahl, who joined RTI in August 1960 and was elected in September 1983 as Institute vice president for environmental sciences and engineering, which he still is.

partitioned into halves. Outfitting for isotopes development laboratory and office space was well along in one half. Ely later recalled that the empty half was ideally suited, and sometimes used, for roller skating.

The saga of the Bacon Street Annex entered a second phase in the summer of 1960, when Ely's group was joined there by RTI's new Natural Products Laboratory (see Chapter 8). By mid-1964 NPL had grown to fill, and soon afterwards to overflow, all available space. Ely moved temporarily to the vacant Wilson Building near RTI's Park campus, and the Institute decided to purchase Bacon Street with a 15-year mortgage. After NPL (by then renamed Chemistry and Life Sciences) moved out to the Park campus in the summer of 1971, the annex stood empty until RTI's customary space pressures peaked once again. The building has since been occupied at various times by environmental sciences, semiconductor research, and chemical engineering, and at the end of 1989 was home to the Center for Process Research and elements of the aerosol technology and environmental risk centers.

Elements of Ely's saga will be touched upon in later pages. Until he retired in March 1983 after nearly 24 years, his energies and abilities molded one of RTI's most versatile careers.

Menius continued to be a powerful influence in Research Triangle affairs until his retirement, in 1981, as dean of N.C. State University's School of Physical and Mathematical Sciences. In 1962-63, at Gov. Terry Sanford's behest, he and Paul Gross of Duke University were the chief architects of the N.C. Board of Science and Technology, the nation's second such state agency and the first to receive substantial state funding. Menius later served twice as a member of RTI's board.

4. It's Official

Although it was a mildly stupendous moment for the principals and their army of volunteers, no fanfare attended the December 29, 1958, filing of RTI's articles of incorporation nor, on the same morning, the charter amendment that changed the name of the Research Triangle Committee to the Research Triangle Foundation.

Neither organization was destined to be out of the public eye for long, however, and a major announcement was scheduled for Friday, January 9, 1959.

One day earlier, faculty members at UNC, Duke, and N.C. State received a memorandum from Duke vice president Paul Gross. It is given verbatim below. Six superscript notations have been inserted. They are keyed to clarifying paragraphs that immediately follow the memo's text.

January 8, 1959

To: MEMBERS OF THE FACULTIES OF DUKE UNIVERSITY THE UNIVERSITY OF NORTH CAROLINA, AND NORTH CAROLINA STATE COLLEGE

An announcement is being made on Friday, January 9, of the establishment of a research institute, to be known as the Research Triangle Institute. The ultimate location of the new institute will be the Research Park at Nelson.[(1)] The Institute is being established by the Research Triangle Foundation[(2)] of North Carolina (formerly the Research Triangle Committee, Inc.)

Nearly two years ago, the undersigned committee was asked by the Research Triangle Committee to study the problem of establishing a research institute, and to make recommendations regarding its nature, structure, personnel and relationship with the three universities. After long study, a report was submitted in the summer of 1958. This report is the basis on which the new research institute is being organized.

This memorandum sets forth in brief form the essentials of the new research institute.

NATURE. The Research Triangle Institute is being established as a contract research agency, to do work for industry and government. It will be similar to Stanford Research Institute in California, Southern Research Institute in Birmingham, Armour Research Institute Foundation in Chicago and several others.

It is hoped through this Institute to provide industry in North Carolina and the South with research services not now available; to encourage the use of research in the State and regional industry; and to extend the Research Triangle's position as a research center.

STRUCTURE. The Research Triangle Institute will be incorporated as a non-profit corporation. There will be no formal or legal association with the universities.[(3)]

The Governing Board will be equally divided between university and non-university representatives. University representatives will include Presidents Friday and Edens, the Chancellors and others.

The Executive Committee[(4)] will include the Vice President in Education and Dean of the University of Duke University; the Vice President for Research and Graduate Studies of the Consolidated University; the Dean of the Graduate School of the University in Chapel Hill; the Dean of the Graduate School of North Carolina State College; the Director of the Research Triangle Foundation;[(5)] the President of the Research Institute; and five representatives of business and industry.

FINANCES. Initial financing of $500,000 has been provided by business and industry in North Carolina. With this aid, it is expected that the Research Institute will reach a currently self-supporting basis in about three years.[(6)] The universities, while having effective control over the policies of the Institute, assume no financial obligation.

RELATIONSHIP WITH UNIVERSITIES. The Research Institute is being established to operate with its own permanent staff and facilities. While certain facilities of the universities may be used initially, through agreement and with proper compensation, these will be interim arrangements.

Where mutual research interests develop between individual faculty members and the Institute, arrangements for implementing these will be made through normal, existing university channels.

PRESIDENT OF THE INSTITUTE. The operating head of the Research Institute will be George R. Herbert. Mr. Herbert is a 1945 graduate of the Naval Academy. He was an instructor in electrical engineering at Michigan State College in 1947-48. In 1948 he joined Stanford Research Institute, then just beginning, as Assistant to the President. From 1953 to 1956 he was Executive Associate Director of Stanford, leaving there in 1956 to go with American and Foreign Power Company in New York City.

Mr. Herbert began his duties on December 1. He was employed on recommendation of the sub-committee for the Research Institute.

LOCATION. The Research Institute will be located in the Research Park in the middle of the Triangle. Temporary quarters will be in the Home Security Life Insurance Company building in Durham. Funds have been provided to begin construction of the first unit of the Institute buildings.

AREAS OF WORK. It is expected that the Institute will engage in work in many areas. The first area of work to be developed is that of statistics. Dr. Gertrude Cox, on part-time leave from North Carolina

> State College, will take the lead in assembling staff for this unit of the Research Institute and in forming programs of work in statistics. Other areas under present consideration are in economics, and in the industrial uses of radioisotope (sic).
>
> THE RESEARCH PARK. Funds have been received on a contributed basis by the Research Triangle Foundation from business and industry in North Carolina sufficient for the Foundation to take over from private ownership the Research Triangle Park. Physical development of the Park will proceed immediately. It is anticipated that land will be sold to industrial concerns for the location of industrial laboratories and associated production activities. Profits from such sales will go to the Research Triangle Foundation, and will be used for the support of research in the Research Triangle area.

The memorandum closed with the typewritten names of the Research Institute Committee members: Whyburn, Gross, Lampe, Reynolds, Armstrong, Simpson, and Hill.

(1) "The Research Triangle Park at Nelson." For most Tarheels the location was moot. Gross put it at Nelson, a community on highway 54 east of the Park and as handy a place as any, although few of his readers could have identified it. The site originally reported by one local newspaper was "in the Lowes Grove area," a community on highway 54 west of the Park. Doubts continue even after the Research Triangle has become North Carolina's most prominent place-name to scientists, scholars, business writers, and corporations around the world. In Raleigh, the daily papers have habitually located the Park "near Raleigh." AP and UPI wire service stories carrying Raleigh datelines usually say "near here." The Durham newspapers take pleasure in putting RTI and the Park "in southern Durham County." As late as 1980 a Duke University news service writer, who didn't bother to look, described them as "near Cary." RTI scrupulously places itself "between Raleigh, Durham, and Chapel Hill," or between NCSU, Duke and UNC-CH.

(2) "The Institute is being established by the Research Triangle Foundation." In a literal sense Gross erred, but understandably, for some previous discussions and written exchanges had postulated that RTI would operate as an arm of, and have its ownership vested in, the Foundation. The outcome was otherwise, and Gross was one of those who made it so. As planned, Institute start-up funding was a grant of $500,000 from private donations made to the Research Triangle Committee/Foundation. However, RTI was in fact jointly "established by" the Consolidated University of North Carolina and Duke University, whose chairmen and presidents signed the articles of incorporation and whose representatives serve on, appoint, or elect all members of RTI's Board of Governors.

(3) "There will be no formal or legal association with the universities." A misconception, for RTI very definitely has formal and legal associations with the universities, which are its joint founders and which, should RTI dissolve, would share the arduous, even onerous task of divvying up its assets. Gross undoubtedly sought to get the point across that RTI was to be a separately-operated, completely self-supporting entity with its own board, management, staff, and facilities, and to assure his faculty colleagues that the universities would not be burdened in any way with their Institute's financial obligations, and that funding resources would not be diverted from the schools to RTI.

(4) In listing some of the original Executive Committee by its members' titles, Gross risked the inference that membership is held by virtue of office. This was not the case then and is not today. There are no *ex officio* Executive Committee members, not even the chairman of the board or the president. All are elected annually by the full Board of Governors.

(5) This individual was George Simpson, who was returning to the UNC sociology faculty after more than two sabbatical years as executive director of the Research Triangle Committee. He stands alone as the one person most responsible for the planning, persuasion, diplomacy, and decisions that shaped and set in motion the entire Research Triangle enterprise. Simpson was RTI's first Executive Committee chairman, serving until September 1962, when he resigned from UNC to become a deputy administrator of NASA and, subsequently, chancellor of the State of Georgia's university system.

(6) "Reach a currently self-supporting basis in about three years." This forecast, agreed to by Simpson's committees and confirmed by Herbert, was right on target. Break-even in financial statement terms was reached early in 1962, a year in which the previous year's contract revenue more than doubled to $1.4 million. Cash break-even, which excludes depreciation charges, had already been achieved. This was a notable milestone, for with no endowment and with draw-downs from the Research Triangle Foundation grant coming to an end, surplus earnings, or profit, were to be RTI's primary source of future funds for building the business through investments in staff, physical facilities, and new research programs.

# # #

Public unveiling of the Research Triangle's initial deeds, as contrasted with its hopes and plans, took place on January 9, 1959, as mentioned in Gross's memo. Held over luncheon at the Sir Walter Hotel in Raleigh, its attendance of more than 200 business, university, and state officials was supplemented by a swarm of newspaper, television, and radio reporters.

Presiding were Governor Hodges and Robert Hanes, the Winston-Salem banker whom Hodges had appointed as chairman of the exploratory Governor's Research Triangle Development Council in the spring of 1955, and of the Research Triangle Committee when it was formed in September 1956.

Their announcements were on the front pages in Raleigh, Durham, and Chapel Hill, and received generous treatment in other parts of the state, too, for all those associated with the Research Triangle, especially Hodges, had stressed from the beginning that the Research Triangle was a statewide undertaking based on statewide assets, and that its anticipated economic impact would benefit all of North Carolina, not just the local communities. Editorial writers heralded the prospect of these benefits, whose accrual in terms of economic expansion, employment, educational improvement, and scientific research has been major news ever since.

The luncheon featured what *The News and Observer* reporter termed "a series of dramatic announcements."

They began with disclosure that a campaign led by Archie K. Davis, who was Hanes' successor as chairman of Wachovia Bank, had successfully raised private donations of $1,425,000 for initial operations, including $500,000 to launch RTI. Later contributions from individual and corporate donors brought the total to $2 million. The campaign's genesis is described in Chapter 9.

George Herbert was introduced to the gathering as president of the new research institute that would bear the Triangle name, and a temporary location for RTI in Durham was announced. This decision typifies the theme of regional unity that so uniquely characterizes the Research Triangle. The Foundation's post office box and telephone exchange were in Raleigh, so the Institute's would be in Durham.

A third bit of news, whose complexities are oversimplified in Chapter 9, was that control of Research Triangle Park acreage had passed from the privately held Pinelands Company to the nonprofit Research Triangle Foundation trusteeship.

Finally, the seriously ill but gratified Hanes was told by Hodges that $300,000 of the donations made by his family, friends, and Winston-Salem businesses were earmarked for a Research Triangle Park headquarters that would be named in his honor. Unfortunately, its sign reads Robert M. Hanes Memorial Building, for he died only two months later.

Governor Hodges was never so right as when he closed the luncheon by calling it "one of the most significant events of recent years in North Carolina," and by singling out Davis, Hanes, and Watts Hill for their "magnificent leadership and unselfish service," although he could easily have expanded his list a dozen times.

Although Hodges was never so right, at that time neither he nor the others knew the half of it, nor could they have guessed at the stunning, all but unbelievable growth that lay ahead.

Two small specks marred the luncheon proceedings, both quite trivial then and now, one of them an irritant still, and both germane to the course of Research Triangle progress.

First was the announcement that a West Coast engineering firm planned a Research Triangle Park location for an eastern office to serve the aircraft and missiles industry. The plans didn't materialize. A disappointment, to be sure, particularly coming so early, but disappointments happen to nonprofit trusteeships just as they do to individuals, families, businesses, and other institutions. In later years, prospective Park occupants brought disappointment by deciding to locate elsewhere, and some that settled in the Park later moved away. Today, as the world knows, Foundation and Park disappointments have been overwhelmed by successes.

The irritant was an incorrect newspaper report that "The Research Triangle Institute is conceived as the housekeeping organization of the entire park development." It was never so conceived, but the myth persisted for years and pops up from time to time even now.

Although similarly named and sharing a common heritage, the Institute and Foundation have no formal ties and totally different purposes. The Foundation promotes, develops, and sells land in the Research Triangle Park. RTI performs scientific research and development services under contract to clients all over the earth. The organizations present a united front, but resemblances in name and function are about the same as those of General Cornwallis and General Motors.

Distinctions between the two blur chiefly in the local area, an irony that earns a brief explanation.

The Foundation's business life began with a bang when the Chemstrand Corporation, a company then jointly owned by Monsanto and American Viscose, announced in May 1959 that it would purchase a 105-acre site for its corporate research center. In September 1960 the first of some 525 employees moved into a multimillion-dollar, 180,000-square-foot laboratory building. Eureka!!

But establishing this wholly new kind of research park proved to be a time-consuming task, especially for a debt-encumbered (see Chapter 9) organization in a location remote from technology-based corporate concentrations. The euphoria that attended Chemstrand's decision was effectively dampened for six long years.

Growth in the Park was very slow. The Robert M. Hanes Memorial Building was completed at the end of 1960. Over the 1961 New Year's weekend, Cox's Statistics Research Division and other researchers, along with RTI administrative offices and the three-person Foundation, moved in. Later in the year the handful of Research Triangle Regional Planning Commission (now Triangle J) employees joined them. In the summer of 1962, the U.S. Forestry Sciences Laboratory, with 24 people, opened across Cornwallis Road from the Hanes Building. In 1963, the State's N.C. Board of Science and Technology came into being, with its research center director's office briefly in Hanes and its seven initial staff engineers in Raleigh. By December 1965 the agency was in its own 20,000-square-foot Park building across Davis Drive from the American Association of Textile Chemists and Colorists, whose staff of 15 occupied a 10,000-square-foot structure completed in the summer of 1964.

The only other non-RTI construction activity in the Park was a 10,000-square-foot shell intended as a swing building for Foundation clients awaiting completion of permanent quarters. It was built by John B. Wilson, a Sperry-Rand subsidiary's executive in Durham and a member of RTI's first Board of Governors, as a means for underlining his confidence in the Research Triangle. An electronics unit of Corning Glass was a brief Wilson Building tenant, and in 1964 Ralph Ely's group, by then renamed Measurements and Controls Laboratory, moved in for a year. In 1965 it was occupied by a computer components division of Technitrol, Inc., which bought the building only to abandon the Park three years later. Since 1974 its owner and occupant has been Troxler Electronic Laboratories, Inc., which has substantially expanded and improved the property.

After six years of near-aridity, 1965 came as a watershed year for Foundation announcements, if not yet for action. In February, the federal government chose a Park site (eventually more than 500 acres) for what would become the National Institute of Environmental Health Sciences (NIEHS). In April, the IBM Corporation made public its intention to purchase 420 acres for a major R&D, engineering, and manufacturing facility. In October, the Beaunit Corporation unveiled plans for a 220,000-square-foot fibers R&D laboratory.

1966 was marked by actions and by more plans. Elements of IBM and NIEHS started arriving. The National Center for Health Statistics moved its data processing center (staff of 81 at the time) to the Park in June. In July, Hercules, Inc., revealed that a large fibers and films research department would open in a new facility of 132,000 square feet.

The Research Triangle Foundation's Park was at last on its way, and in very big style.

During all the slow motion from 1959 to 1966, meanwhile, the Research Triangle Institute was humming, as it still is. Announcements were made about statistics and isotopes research, about other new research programs, about new research contract acquisitions, about State of North Carolina equipment grants, about a very large private foundation grant, about a series of senior staff appointments. Other noticeable events were RTI's lease of the Bacon Street Annex in 1959 and its move from downtown Durham to the Park at the beginning of 1961.

By 1966 the construction of four more RTI laboratory and research office buildings in the Park had been not only announced, but completed.

Throughout these many months RTI was perhaps a dominant element in Research Triangle Park activity and public attention. For the local communities and news media, up until the thunderous NIEHS and IBM announcements, Chemstrand and RTI *were* the Park. Herbert was in continual demand as a Research Triangle spokesman; after all, RTI was keeping to a strenuous, well-publicized pace, and he was at its head. Newspapers and magazines throughout the state carried interviews with him, and he was swamped with speaking invitations. During RTI's first 18 months he averaged one talk per week, mostly for professional and civic clubs, but also for educational and economic development groups and a seasoning of miscellaneous. The rate of nontechnical speaking engagements for him and others from RTI scarcely diminished until the late 1970s, although no one kept count.

In interviews and talks Herbert invariably stressed that RTI was but one aspect of the larger Research Triangle concept. Almost always his remarks began with descriptions of the Foundation's, the Park's, and the universities' roles, with particulars about RTI operations kept for the end. But despite his and others' meticulous care in giving clear definition to the Research Triangle's separate parts, North Carolinians tended to retain the notion that Foundation, Park, and Institute were synonymous, and that RTI was the engine pulling all else up the hill.

To a minor extent, during those early days, this was true, a fact that helps to maintain the confusion, for in the beginning an acknowledged and major mission for RTI was to be the focal point around which the Park would grow. In this role, RTI's announcements and activities were meant to provide visible, tangible evidence to the world and to potential occupants that the Research Triangle Park was for real and that something was indeed happening out there in those all but empty acres that once were, in Pearson Stewart's phrase, "useful mostly for holding two counties together."

The Park's germination period was, however, longer than many people expected, even though others closer to the situation knew well enough that they were committed to a future 5, 10, or 15 years down the road. By the time that future flowered many, even most, local observers were accustomed to the harmless but mistaken idea that Foundation, Park, and Institute are one and the same.

Not that it matters, for there's more than enough glory to spread around, with plenty to spare.

5. Getting Started

There wasn't a vote, according to Simpson, but by September of 1958 it was clear that the Research Institute Committee wanted George Herbert as Institute executive. Letters of recommendation were solicited, the president of American and Foreign Power Company gave permission for his treasurer to be approached.

With good reason Herbert "suffered the agonies of the damned" when confronted with Watts Hill's formal job offer. After all, he had been with American and Foreign Power only a scant two years, it was among the world's half-dozen largest electric utility holding companies, with operating subsidiaries throughout Latin American, and he had a clear shot at a vice presidency in New York headquarters or the presidency of one of the subsidiaries. Still, this North Carolina belief in and dedication to a Research Triangle amounted both to rare opportunity and to a one-of-a-kind challenge, intangibles irresistible to Herbert's adventurous soul. Adventurous, yes, and tireless, too; habitually optimistic, but never hasty.

Simpson, Hill, Gross, and other committee members weren't hasty, either. During April and May they invited senior officers of several not-for-profit institutes for lengthy discussions about research operations and prospects, financing, staff, administrative functions, the attributes of a president. These officials, scientists all, provided valuable insights into the start-up and development of the Midwest, Southern, Southwest, and Armour research institutes, those with a regional flavor. They were helpful and encouraging. Gertrude Cox visited Stanford Research Institute (SRI) in May and found a similarly positive response.

In June the committee brought in Jesse E. Hobson for similar but more detailed talks. It was Hobson, a former director of Armour, who went west in 1948 to infuse a young and tottering SRI with the force and vision that propelled it to eminence by 1956, when he resigned to become vice president and research director at the United Fruit Company in Boston.

Hobson was characteristically thorough and engaging in his talks with the committee. He endorsed the other consultants' appraisal of the Research Triangle's feasibility, and he also went a couple of steps farther. First, if he were to take the job, which wasn't offered, it would be as head of the foundation, and he listed several names for consideration as president of the institute, which was then seen as a subsidiary. Next, one of his earliest actions would be to hire a business manager. He recommended that the committee invite his candidate for a visit.

Herbert was glad to oblige as a favor to Hobson, but hadn't the slightest intention of working for him. He'd done that already, as Hobson's right hand through eight hectic years at SRI, from the cliff-hanging days of Hobson's rescue mission there (which included a baby-faced, 26-year-old Herbert going up against six San Francisco banking tycoons for an unsecured emergency loan of $600,000) to the later era of rocketing success. Success or anything else with Hobson was invariably a rocketing, racking, high wire, pressure-intense business. So is RTI.

Both the committee and Herbert liked what they saw. For him, Simpson's imaginative and careful planning, and Hill's evident enthusiasm and purposefulness were convincing. So were assurances of unconditional university support given by Duke's Gross and UNC's Friday, and Wachovia Bank chairman Archie Davis's assurance that sufficient funds would be on hand to cover the Institute's operating deficit and a first building.

For the committee, Herbert's modest demeanor, his quiet self-confidence, his record of managing people, programs, and money at Stanford, and his management of American and Foreign Power's millions were uniformly attractive. Perhaps they sensed in him what William H. Prescott, writing more than a hundred years earlier, had observed of Cortés, that "He combined what is most rare, singular coolness and constancy of purpose with a spirit of enterprise that might well be called romantic." In any event, the committee was moved to reassess the qualifications demanded of a chief executive.

Right from the start Simpson had always averred that this person "shall be [a scientist] of high scholarly stature." Neither in 1958 nor at any other time has Herbert pretended to such a distinction, asserting all along that his role at RTI is "to recruit the best available scientists, and then get out of their way." An electrical engineering graduate of the Naval Academy, his technical experience was limited to one academic year as an EE instructor at Michigan State.

The scientist of stature requirement faded as Simpson, Hill, and the others took the measure of Herbert's personal traits and management abilities. He had started at SRI as an assistant to Hobson, rose to manager of business operations, and was executive associate director, number 2, during his final two years. The earlier job titles weren't close to describing what he did. He was chiefly responsible for coping with a high-powered board and an often touchy Stanford University administration. He was in essence SRI's treasurer. He was entrusted with writing key policy papers and with keeping the confidences of staff members from top to bottom. He ran SRI's offices of accounting, contracts, personnel, purchasing, maintenance, security. Except for exclusively technical matters, he was in on all major decisions. Research managers and senior scientists early on found him quick to grasp their ideas and specialized vocabularies, able to help substantially in new contract acquisition and negotiation and in customer relations, prudent in financial matters but aggressive in providing the ways and means to build and maintain a productive research environment.

Scientists of stature were in abundance at the founding universities and could be relied upon for counsel and action whenever needed. So Herbert entered the Research Triangle picture.

He and Hill didn't sign an employment agreement until November 1, but the Research Institute Committee, the Research Triangle Committee, the governor, and other interested parties knew a month earlier that they had their president. Herbert knew it, too. Indeed, with his easy tolerance for protocol he wrote to Hill in mid-October that he had "authorized—I don't know by what authority—Buck Menius to prepare an Institute proposal to the AEC."

Based on Stanford Research Institute's headlong evolvement from a San Francisco Bay Area institution serving California industry to one serving public and private clients worldwide, Herbert expressed a minor reservation about the Research Triangle committees' emphasis on research goals within North Carolina. He knew that with a contract sponsorship limited primarily to the state, or even to the south, an institute couldn't achieve stability and probably wouldn't survive. This doubt was washed away in a stroke when Governor Hodges told him that "Activities of the Institute can go as far afield as opportunity and ability warrant, as long as they reflect credit back on North Carolina and the Research Triangle."*

Herbert officially began as RTI's first employee on December 1, 1958, before there was either a legal corporate employer or money for a payroll. It may be, as he said much later, that he "was brave enough, or foolish enough, or simply had the dumb good luck to sign up for ID card #1," but whatever it was he had no trouble keeping busy. High on the list was completing the final draft of Menius's AEC proposal. With the help of Home Security Life's chairman and principal stockholder, Watts Hill, a lease was signed for the unoccupied second floor of the company's new building at 505 West Chapel Hill Street in Durham. Post Office Box 490 was rented. A telephone was installed on January 21, one of 1,977 connections made in Durham that year.

*Hodges meant it. The next November he told a group of Swiss businessmen meeting in Zurich that "North Carolina, through such efforts as the Research Triangle Institute, is extending its interests and its horizons far beyond the borders of the state and the nation."

It's likely that none of the new listings held greater significance for the city, the region, or the state than 6712.

Then there were meetings to attend. With Simpson, Hill, and other committee members singly and together. With new friends, faculty members, and academic officials at all three campuses, where none could foretell that in coming years all three would accord him honorary degrees. With Research Triangle Foundation and Park officers about a schedule of advances from the $500,000 set aside for RTI's initial funding from the $2,000,000 raised by Davis. With the same individuals about a mode for deeding Park acreage to RTI, and about Hanes Building design and space allocations. With Cox and others relative to transfer of the Survey Operations Unit. With Hodges about many things, including arrangements for the January 9 announcement luncheon.* With Durham businessmen in anticipation of space needs for the Isotopes Development Laboratory. With lawyers about RTI's articles of incorporation and by-laws. With Blue Cross about a hospital and health care program, and with other insurers about liability and fidelity coverage. With state cabinet officers and legislators in Raleigh. Herbert also prepared a provisional operating budget of $63,100 for the first quarter of 1959. As usual with him, there was time for everything.

Bill Perkins showed up for work on February 9 and opened an RTI faith-and-hope bank account with the Foundation's first $60,000. With Herbert temporarily in an upper floor office, Perkins for a couple of weeks had Home Security Life's second floor all to himself. Its 10,000 square feet gave him what was probably the largest private office east of Hollywood, or at least Houston.

The two of them had all they could do just to stay close to even with housekeeping duties, Bacon Street construction plans, setting up procedures for accounting, contracts, personnel, for purchasing, and for getting paid. Office partitions had to be selected, ordered, and installed. Nancy Campbell's desk had to be uncrated.

Meanwhile, outside demands on Herbert's time were mounting from university groups, the governor's office, Foundation visitors, the press, and civic and professional groups throughout the state. All were legitimate, all were in RTI's and the Triangle's best interest, and all were met.

But the two men and two secretaries needed help. Herbert didn't wait long, only until mid-April, to ease the situation by sending for a former Stanford Research Institute colleague and Naval Academy classmate, Samuel C. Ashton, to become RTI's administrator and treasurer. Ashton had been an

* January 9 was a chock-full Friday. RTI's Board of Governors had its first meeting at 10:00 a.m. and its second at 11:15. At 2:30 the board's Executive Committee met for the first time.

assistant director of physical sciences, one of SRI's four main research units, he knew the ropes of running one of those strange creatures called not-for-profit research institutes, and he was, as he put it, "Ready to start making my own mistakes." Ashton became a vice president the next year, and until his death in 1987 he at one time or another held management responsibility for every administrative, support, and service function. Of more lasting consequence, he oversaw campus planning and the design and construction of RTI's first 16 buildings.

On the research front, RTI was moving into high gear by the summer of 1959 and seems destined to stay there forever. Cox, with Finkner joining her in April, both of them half-time, was hiring statistical and survey scientists, and exploiting her entree to potential clients in civilian and military government agencies and in industry. Ely was also hiring staff and becoming familiar with state and regional manufacturing firms, predominantly in textiles, furniture and timber, cigarettes, and paper. Herbert, Simpson, the board, and appropriate faculty members were sorting out the options and opportunities for new research directions.

In this regard the universities, and particularly the RTI board's Executive Committee, have always been active in any organizational initiatives or restructuring that may lead to a broadening of scientific capability and subject matter undertakings. It was so in the spring of 1958 with Colvard and Cox in statistics, with Menius and isotopes in the fall and, a year later, with Armstrong and polymers (see Chapter 7). As policy, and in practical terms as well, this involvement has had a profound influence on shaping RTI's sound and healthy growth.

RTI's entry into statistics, isotopes, and polymer research sprang from what were basically outside circumstances or interests, the first two being set in motion not casually, by any means, but without benefit of a considered corporate judgment or plan. From the spring of 1959 onwards, the setting of new research directions and marketing goals has followed a more deliberative process.

Drawing on the advice of their not-for-profit consultants, whose views were strongly reinforced by Herbert, the RTI founders fashioned a concept for a research institute that would serve a varied, national clientele in a variety of disciplines and subjects. They envisioned programs in both the soft, paper sciences and in the hard, laboratory sciences.

For the former, statistics research was an ideal beginning, especially because it built on a well-established reputation and met the Research Institute Committee's criteria of being able to begin in minimum time and at reasonable cost.

Isotopes development was ideal, too, for it met a specific Atomic Energy Commission goal and was assured of ample, sustained AEC funding. Other laboratory research—chemistry, engineering, the life sciences—might not come so easily. It would also require costly equipment and instrumentation.

RTI's third research division came about through a combination of the need to grow and diversify, the necessity of doing so through the low-investment soft sciences, the U.S. Air Force, and the ever-present, invaluable university connection.

Quite a number of Triangle university faculty, Al Finkner among them, were members of a local Air Force operations analysis reserve unit. Their commander was George E. Nicholson, Jr., head of the UNC-Chapel Hill Department of Statistics, where Cox's survey staff had been housed. He wasn't on any of the Research Triangle committees, but like many others at the three campuses he was close to the situation, eager to help, and aware that an economics-oriented research program was being considered. Economics or a related discipline had been recommended by the not-for-profit consultants; Herbert was keenly aware of the conspicuous success it had enjoyed at Stanford.

Calling on his Air Force acquaintanceships, Nicholson suggested that Hugh J. Miser might be interested. He was a mathematician and at that time deputy director and acting chief of the Air Force Operations Analysis Division in Washington. Herbert drove to Miser's home in Vienna, Virginia, for an initial interview. At RTI's first staff meeting a few weeks later, held on May 4, 1959, and attended by all but two of the Institute's ten employees, he announced that an Operational Sciences Laboratory would be formed in June. Projected research topics included inventory control, work-flow analysis, production scheduling, warehousing, some defense work. Contract acquisition proved disappointingly slow, however, and although there were several promising prospects only three projects were on the books by the following May, when Miser resigned to accept an appointment at MIT.

Locating a successor became an important agenda item for Herbert and a primary duty for Hugh W. Hunter. Thanks again to the university connection, Hunter had joined RTI on September 1, 1959, as senior scientist for engineering and physical sciences. This was the Institute's top research slot, acknowledged by Herbert and the board as both vital and difficult to fill. In addition to having proven administrative skills, the successful candidate's scientific bona fides would be subject to close university scrutiny.

Hunter survived it all very nicely. A physicist whose Ph.D. was from Indiana University, he conducted wartime research at both Cal and Cal Tech, then in 1948 became a staff scientist for the U.S. Naval Ordnance Testing

Station at China Lake, California. At the time he first heard of RTI he had risen to head the NOTS propulsion systems R&D programs, running a staff of 550.

The contact came about through William M. Whyburn, a mathematician and a member of a China Lake advisory committee. Whyburn also just happened to be the UNC General Administration's vice president for research and graduate studies, had served on the Research Institute Committee throughout its existence, and in 1959 was a member of RTI's board and Executive Committee. His admiration for Hunter's personal and professional qualities obviously carried weight. So Herbert visited Hunter, and Hunter visited North Carolina, decided to stay, and remained as RTI's chief scientific officer for nearly six years before returning to NOTS as its research director.

Hunter didn't arrive in time to help celebrate the completion of RTI's first research report at the end of July. It dealt with a survey of Raleigh residents who were interviewed about their attitudes toward public education. Conducted for Stanford University's Communication Research Institute (no relation to SRI), it was RTI's first education-related project. Piling up the firsts as things got going, it was also the first of hundreds of survey projects to garner a participation rate of 90 percent or more. From a sample of 1,274 individuals, 929 were found to be eligible as registered voters, and interviews were obtained with 846, a response rate of 91 percent.

RTI's statisticians, survey designers, and field interviewing teams have, since the beginning, made the Institute one of the world's premier survey research organizations by any standard.

The second educational project was also completed, after an eight-month effort, in 1959. The National Science Foundation engaged RTI to design a survey and conduct interviews with participants in two NSF programs aimed at improving teacher-pupil relationships in science education. RTI's assignment at 103 sites nationwide was to gather data about individuals' experiences in both programs, then to evaluate their effectiveness and to suggest methods for enabling the NSF to measure the programs' progress and achievement. Education research has been almost continuous ever since, much of it relating to science instruction and to student enrollment in science courses.

RTI ended its first operating year of 1959 with contract revenue of $142,412 and a staff of 35. Research professionals included 10 statisticians, 1 economist, 7 engineers, 2 physicists, and 1 chemist.

6. Setting the Stage: II. The Not-for-Profit Institutes

Seven multiclient, multidisciplinary, not-for-profit scientific research institutes* in the United States account for only a tiny fraction—not quite eight-tenths of one percent—of the $130 billion R&D expenditure being made annually by American industry and government. Their 1988 combined contract revenue total was about $905 million.

Yet as a nucleus of innovative research enterprise, their influence on scientific leadership, on technological policy and progress, and on the national economy far exceeds this dollar measure.

The two oldest are the Battelle Memorial Institute, which started in Columbus, Ohio, in 1929, and the Illinois Institute of Technology Research Institute, formerly the Armour Research Foundation, started in Chicago in 1936.

Within two years following the end of World War II, several other institutes had come into being on the wave of scientific R&D needs and opportunities that resulted from wartime programs in aviation, communications, radar, the new science of operations research, and the new world of nuclear research.

Among these new institutes were Midwest, started in 1944 in Kansas City, Missouri; Southern, 1945, in Birmingham; Stanford, 1946, now SRI International, in Menlo Park, California; and Southwest, 1947, in San Antonio.

The seven not-for-profits have no organizational ties or formal relationships, but numerous resemblances are evident in their broad areas of interest, methods of operations, and problem-solving orientation. From their various locations and out of their various origins, they serve generally similar groups of research clients and research objectives.

George Herbert has summarized their similarities, beginning with the not-for-profit designation. If an institute is to survive, it must be either endowed or subsidized or it must, like any successful business, operate in the black. The legal distinction is that the profits or net earnings of a not-for-profit institute cannot be disbursed for the benefit of individuals. Any surplus is

* Research institutes that operate within the structure of a university or an industry, or predominantly on behalf of a federal agency, are not included in this discussion.

instead put back into the organization for facilities expansion, for supplementing research grant funding, or for other public purposes.

A second characteristic by which Herbert distinguishes the not-for-profits from normal businesses is that they were created solely to serve others—industry and federal, state, and local governments—and not to engage in R&D for their own institutional benefit.

Writing for *Science* magazine in 1983, Sherwood L. Fawcette, who was then Battelle's chairman and chief executive, observed other features common to the not-for-profits:

> These institutes have grown and flourished because they meet real needs of industry and government; they are eminently practical. By their nature, they offer scientists an alternative to research careers in either an academic institution, a government laboratory, or a captive research center of private industry. The independent institutes have their greatest appeal for the scientist who enjoys the challenge of being an entrepreneur, of identifying a real-world need, selling the idea to a company or government agency, and leading the research to fill that need. This is a kind of research that calls for alertness to change, sensitivity to market forces, and innovation. Some scientists find this environment exciting; others find it frightening.

Another shared attribute of the not-for-profits is that as corporate entities they were formed to maintain the diverse staff and facilities necessary to provide research and development services under contract to clients ranging from small industrial concerns to the largest corporations and government agencies.

The pre-World War II institutes were formed largely along disciplinary lines as adjuncts to basic research at universities and the then-existing handful of major industrial laboratories.

War's exigencies effectively dispelled any notion that science lives in ivory towers apart from the rest of the world. The institutes of the early post-war years were a powerful mechanism in effecting the exchanges between laboratory and marketplace that marked the beginnings of the technology-based industrial economy in mid-century America. They pioneered in using the fact-finding approach of science to solve new technical, economic, and social problems. They pioneered in the use of applied research techniques for helping business and government alike to identify, to measure, and to meet technical, economic, and social opportunities.

While retaining the commitment of the older organizations to undertake broad research programs that would increase the nation's scientific resources and serve national purposes, RTI was also a strikingly novel kind of economic asset consciously created in and for North Carolina. The locations of the older institutes were not accidental, but location was incidental to such other considerations as convenience, the community and civic interests of institute founders, existing and potential industrial demand, or parallel but separate university activities.

As the first addition to the not-for-profit family in a dozen years, RTI was something different. Its conception and formation as a part of the larger Research Triangle effort were entirely and exclusively within the context of North Carolina's special needs and special resources. It sprang from statewide recognition of statewide problems, and from a statewide determination to surmount them.

7. What Jean Dreyfus Boissevain Did

What Jean Dreyfus Boissevain did "more than any other single event assured our success," Herbert has stated.

Her action came soon after she had inspected RTI's expanse of nothing on September 17, 1959, and it assures her a prominent place front-and-center in any reckoning of RTI's "most" people.

What she decided upon was approval of a $2.5 million grant to RTI for creation of a scientific memorial to her late husband Camille Dreyfus, founder and chairman of the Celanese Corporation of America, now Hoechst-Celanese.

Made in the name of the Camille and Henry Dreyfus Foundation, the grant provided $500,000 for a building, $200,000 for equipment, and $1,800,000 to support an initial ten-year program of basic research in polymer physics and chemistry.

Twenty-five years later, Herbert wrote to Mrs. Boissevain that "I still have vivid memories of your 1959 visit, when the then-new Research Triangle Institute could be described only as embryonic, and the research park that was to grow around us was nothing but empty pine land. From the window beside my desk I can see the small hillside where we stood while I pointed out the site on which we proposed to build the laboratory in the middle of a campus that did not exist. With the passage of time, my admiration for your confidence in us has grown almost to a sense of awe."

The hillside was just south of Cornwallis Road near what would become its intersection with Davis Drive. Mrs. Boissevain's confidence in RTI was an act of faith that echoes still.

The Dreyfus Foundation board of trustees, with Mrs. Boissevain as its president, envisioned far more than a steel and plaster monument, which would have to be seen to be appreciated. The trustees' primary goal was a memorial to keep the name of Camille Dreyfus alive through advances in fundamental polymer research.

Their "belief that the memory of a creative genius can best be truly honored and perpetuated . . . by continued creative work to broaden the horizons of knowledge" was complemented by RTI's belief, as stated in the grant proposal, that the combination of ". . . fundamental research, dissemination of scientific information, and encouragement of promising young scientists can do more than any single program [can] to further the basic goals of the Dreyfus Foundation, thereby creating, in honor of Dr. Camille Dreyfus, a memorial which will . . . in the years ahead . . . attract the attention and recognition of the international scientific community to which he so richly contributed."

Fine words, and fully matched by deeds "in the years ahead."

Objectives were more clearly defined in a statement of operating principles that RTI followed throughout the life of the grant. The Dreyfus Foundation and RTI agreed that "The laboratory will be devoted to conducting fundamental research in the science of polymers; publishing the results of the research for general dissemination to scientists throughout the world; and advancing scientific knowledge of this field. The results of such research will be published as papers originating from the Camille Dreyfus Laboratory of the Research Triangle Institute. Additional objectives of the laboratory's polymer program will be to provide fellowships for scientists from throughout the world, to stimulate greater interest in polymer science, and to encourage potential scientists to select careers in this field."

The Dreyfus grant announcement, made by Hodges and Herbert at a news conference on October 28, 1959, was a smash hit in the Triangle area and throughout the state. Hodges, who had entertained Mrs. Boissevain and other foundation trustees at the Governor's Mansion a month earlier, hailed the grant as "one of the greatest things that has happened in North Carolina."

A great thing it certainly was for those faculty members and businessmen who had launched RTI and for the Institute's staff of 30. The vast majority of them, and of other enthusiastic North Carolinians as well, couldn't have defined a polymer—although they wore man-made polymers, sat and slept on man-made polymers, ate and drank from man-made polymers, and drove cars fitted inside and out with man-made polymers—but those who had any stake in RTI as founders, fans, or employees, were elated to find their own commitments resoundingly endorsed by the Dreyfus trustees to the tune of $2.5 million (the equivalent of about $10.7 million in 1989) and the accompanying pledge to a new endeavor in scientific excellence.

The great news in North Carolina came as surprising news to the world community of scientists involved with polymer research and the development of polymer-based products and systems. One and all could only admire the intent to create America's first laboratory devoted solely and equally to fundamental research in the chemistry and physics of polymers; none could question the desire to commemorate the name of one of chemistry's and the chemical industry's pioneers. What caused eyebrows to rise were the identity and location of the Dreyfus Foundation's first major memorial award recipient.

Within just a few years, however, it was the rare polymer scientist who had to ask, "Two and a half million dollars for who? Where?" By then, the Research Triangle Institute, its Camille Dreyfus Laboratory, and their North Carolina location were fixtures on the international polymer research map.

With the ball in RTI's court, the Research Triangle Foundation speedily arranged the transfer to RTI of 16.29 acres as the site for the Camille Dreyfus Laboratory building, architects' proposals were invited, and Herbert began an 18-month search of the United States and Europe for the internationally recognized scientist who would be the laboratory's director.

Wonderful news that the Dreyfus grant was, its origin predated by many months Mrs. Boissevain's visit to RTI in September 1959. To RTI's great good fortune, a key figure, more properly the key figure, was Robert T. Armstrong. He possessed striking qualifications for the role. An organic chemist with a Ph.D. from MIT and several years of industrial experience, his World War II work on the vulcanization of rubber won wide attention, particularly from Camille Dreyfus and Celanese. Armstrong joined the company in 1946 and rose through various posts, including head of the Celanese R&D operation in Charlotte. It was in this position that he became a member of the original Research Triangle Committee in 1955, a capacity he retained after being promoted to New York as vice president for research. He was elected to RTI's initial board and Executive Committee in January 1959, serving until his retirement from Celanese in 1974.

The Armstrong connection proved fruitful for both RTI and the Dreyfus Foundation. His converging interests under several headings were persuasive factors in the foundation's RTI decision. These included his scientist's interest in supporting basic research, his corporate interest in creating a suitable memorial to Dr. Dreyfus, his personal interest in perpetuating the name of the man who had been his mentor, and his public service interest in fostering RTI.

Although Armstrong was not then a member of the Dreyfus Foundation board, he was intent on promoting the trustees' goal of an as yet unspecified memorial project. As senior technical officer at Celanese, moreover, his recommendations on the foundation's educational and scientific investments were sought and welcomed by the trustees. Even before moving to North Carolina, Herbert had, in December 1958, discussed with Armstrong his conviction that "To the extent feasible, a solid operating base of reasonably long-term, fundamental research is necessary if RTI is to contribute to the growth of true scientific research in our region, if we are to attract the consulting participation of university faculty members, and if we are to attract the attention of the national scientific community to North Carolina."

Armstrong's response was positive. He explained that Dreyfus Foundation activities were limited largely to educational grants for worthy students, and that the trustees had considered, but rejected, many university requests for endowments or building donations. They felt that Camille Dreyfus's fame was international and would not be properly recognized by gifts to a single school.

When Herbert decided to go for it, Armstrong worked with him on RTI's grant proposal and in convincing the Dreyfus Foundation trustees that their memorial aims would be fully realized through creation of a Camille Dreyfus Laboratory dedicated to fundamental research in polymer science.

RTI's quest for a polymer scientist of international stature as Camille Dreyfus Laboratory director began immediately after the grant award.

Herbert was principally assisted by Armstrong in this two-continent survey, but there was other help, too, in the form of consultation and advice from 18 top scientists, most of them on more than one occasion, from university, government, and industry polymer research programs.

Among them were four of especially outstanding caliber who were soon enlisted as a scientific advisory committee for the duration of the grant: Herman F. Mark, director of polymer research at the Polytechnic Institute of Brooklyn; Sir Harry W. Melville, Secretary of the United Kingdom's Department of Scientific and Industrial Research; Charles J. Overberger, head of the Chemistry Department at Brooklyn Poly; and George J. Smets, director of macromolecular chemistry at the University of Louvain in Belgium. They were joined in 1966 by A. Caress, retired R&D director of Imperial Chemical Industries, Inc., in London.

Amidst innumerable other organizational, promotional, planning, and research project details that pressed for his attention, the rich harvest of reputation promised by the Dreyfus Foundation award spurred Herbert to give high priority to the search for the eminent scientist who would be head of RTI's Camille Dreyfus Laboratory. While Armstrong and other advisers were particularly helpful in screening applicants and recommending candidates, the tasks of deciding whom to interview, and then making arrangements to do so, inevitably fell to Herbert. His travels in this undertaking took him to many destinations in the U.S. and Europe, and gave him a superb introductory course in polymer science.

After more than a year, by the end of 1960, the choice had finally narrowed to a highly regarded Yugoslav theoretical physicist and mathematician. This was Anton Peterlin, Ph.D. from Humboldt University in Berlin in 1938, appointed to the university faculty in his native Ljubljana in 1939, imprisoned by Italian occupation forces in 1942 and again by the German army in 1944, full professor of physics at war's end in 1945. In 1949, at the halfway point of his 21-year tenure at the University of Ljubljana, he was the founder, and for ten years the director, of the Yugoslav atomic energy commission's J. Stefan Institute for nuclear reactor research. His selection was endorsed enthusiastically by all concerned, with Gross calling the candidate's qualifications "formidable."

But Herbert's search wasn't ended, for Peterlin proved to be elusive prey. He had left Ljubljana for visiting professorships at Harvard, the University of Mainz in West Germany, and Wayne State University in Detroit, but colleagues at the J. Stefan Institute didn't know his present whereabouts. Herbert's pursuit led him first to Strasbourg, France, where a second clue sent him on to Mainz. From Mainz he ran his quarry to earth at last in Munich where, since the fall of 1960, Peterlin had been contentedly established as Institute of Physics head at the Technische Hochschule, or technical university, his contentment buttressed by the knowledge that funding had been authorized for acquisition of a nuclear magnetic resonance spectrometer.

Herbert is nothing if not persuasive, however, the Dreyfus grant was a convincing carrot, and Peterlin agreed to make a January 1961 visit to the United States. He was wined and dined by RTI, the Dreyfus Foundation, and Celanese in New York, Washington, and Charlotte. In Charlotte, Herbert has been fond of saying, Peterlin had an experience that may have been the clincher on his decision to accept RTI's offer: his first grits.

The acceptance was short-lived. Amid doubts and misgivings, Peterlin withdrew it soon after returning home. Herbert is nothing if not resolute, however, and he set off once more for Munich to convince the Peterlins to change their minds. One of his ploys was to brainwash their young daughter and son with a wonders-and-glories hard-sell about growing up in America. Another was to match the Munich university's promise to buy a nuclear magnetic resonance spectrometer, although he had only the sketchiest notion of an NMR's uses or cost. This pledge was made good in November, Herbert learning in the process that a Varian DP-60 NMR Spectrometer could be had for $46,178.95, including tax.

Peterlin's appointment was announced on May 15, 1961. RTI's news release carried the "Research Triangle Park, N.C." dateline for the first time in history and it so ran in the *New York Herald-Tribune* and via the United Press wire in other newspapers. The announcement also received good attention from technical periodicals, including the American Chemical Society's weekly *Chemical & Engineering News*, in whose Washington office Herbert typed a tailor-made version.

By the time Peterlin's name appeared on RTI's roster the first of September, Howard G. Clark, a former Chemstrand chemist, had been working in the Bacon Street Annex for nearly a year on a couple of Dreyfus Foundation projects dealing with polymer synthesis and structure. Clark has now been a Duke University professor of biomedical engineering for many years. In 1966, Peterlin named him to head a new medical polymers section within the Camille Dreyfus Laboratory (CDL). The section's initial research, sponsored by the National Institutes of Health, focused on improving the membrane materials used in hemodialysis treatments for kidney disease patients. After more than two decades, medical polymers are still an active and newsworthy part of RTI research.

Coming aboard at the same time as Peterlin was Vivian T. Stannett, recruited by Herbert as associate director of CDL for polymer chemistry. Peterlin would manage the laboratory's general affairs and scientific programs while concentrating his personal research on fundamental studies in polymer physics.

Over the years, Stannett fashioned a remarkable career, with a heavy emphasis on Dreyfus. When Herbert first contacted him at the suggestion of N.C. State colleagues, Stannett had for nine years been a professor at the State University of New York's College of Forestry in Syracuse. After receiving a chemistry degree in London, his first job, and first Dreyfus association, was with British Celanese, founded by Camille Dreyfus's brother Henry. Following wartime service in ordnance with the Ministry of Supply, he came to America for his Ph.D. at the Polytechnic Institute of Brooklyn.

His six years at RTI's Camille Dreyfus Laboratory ended in 1967 when he was appointed to the endowed Camille Dreyfus professorship of chemical engineering at N.C. State University. In 1975 he became NCSU's vice provost and graduate dean, serving for 13 years and garnering a hatful of scientific honors. And, like Gertrude Cox before him, he received the O. Max Gardner Award from the state university system's board of governors.

Stannett also has the distinction of being the first of two former employees to become members of RTI's own board and Executive Committee, posts he held from 1975 to 1982. The other is Larry K. Monteith, chancellor at N.C. State University and former dean of the College of Engineering.

Upon the award of the Dreyfus Foundation grant, Herbert, Ashton, and Hill lost no time in beginning to translate faith and $2.5 million into an international center for polymer research. Within ten months an architect had been retained, perennial building chairman Hill had taken the plans to New York for Mrs. Boissevain's approval, site preparation was completed, and construction had begun under Ashton's supervision and Hill's gimlet eye. The name "Camille Dreyfus Laboratory" stays with the building for as long as it stands.

Plans called for a one-story structure of 40,000 square feet erected as a hollow square around a 12-sided auditorium. The grant provided $500,000 for the first 20,000 square feet and the auditorium. It took $1.3 million in reserve and borrowed funds to complete the second 20,000 square feet in 1978.

Work crews put their finishing touches on the building at about two a.m. on November 10, 1961, leaving RTI personnel loads of time to prepare for the dedication ceremonies scheduled at four o'clock that afternoon in the auditorium.

Guests included Dreyfus Foundation officers (but Mrs. Boissevain had to send regrets), the chairman, president, and vice chairman of Celanese, local university and government officials, the director of the National Bureau of Standards, scientific and chemical industry dignitaries, RTI staff and board members, and representatives of Research Triangle Park neighbors, meaning Chemstrand. Governor Terry Sanford came from Raleigh, and U.S. Secretary of Commerce Luther Hodges came from Washington, D.C., to deliver dedicatory remarks. The date was just two years and two weeks after he had announced the Dreyfus grant as "one of the greatest things that has happened in North Carolina." (At a banquet in Durham that evening, Paul Gross presided and Sir Harry Melville was on hand from England to speak.)

The auditorium has been in almost continuous use ever since. Reserved primarily for Institute business, it is also available to outside nonprofit groups such as technical society chapters, school and other professional associations, and area public service and civic agencies. Its convenience for Triangle-wide gatherings, especially those involving the universities, has made the Camille Dreyfus auditorium a boon to its many Research Triangle area users.

The Dreyfus Foundation's charge that RTI's Camille Dreyfus Laboratory should be devoted to fundamental research, publication, information exchange, and the training of an international cadre of polymer scientists was totally to Peterlin's taste. Through the ten-year life of the original research grant, and for four more years under a terminal $400,000 award, he led his associates to an exceptional record. Consider:

The grant agreement emphasized dissemination of basic research results. Over the years, a CDL staff that averaged 13 Ph.D. and four M.S. professionals disseminated their research results by publishing 404 papers in the scientific literature, not including preprints, individual chapters for books edited by others, or book coauthorship, and through 632 lectures in university, industry, and government settings in the U.S. and abroad, not counting those given at RTI.

They received information, too, which is also dissemination. Visiting polymer specialists, 88 of them from abroad, gave 228 formal lectures for RTI staff, university faculty, and other Triangle area scientists. Including the 88, seminars and visits of a few days to a few weeks brought 420 foreign scientists to RTI from Canada, England, Scotland, ten countries of Western and Central Europe, Australia, Japan, India, and Israel.

In addition to Peterlin himself, RTI brought a number of polymer scientists to America. Several returned to their native lands after a few years, but others went on to senior university positions or to industry. One who remains at RTI making significant research advances after 26 years is senior physicist and electron microscopy specialist Peter Ingram, who attracted Peterlin's attention on the strength of a doctoral dissertation written at the University of Southampton in England. Anton Schindler, a native of Austria and at RTI for 27 years in 1989, can't be properly included in this category, but certainly rates a mention anyway. A physical chemist and an RTI principal scientist, he came to the U.S. to join the Koppers Company.

While the Dreyfus Foundation's annual funding sustained CDL's general program, substantial support also came from the Celanese Corporation, which pledged and gave one million dollars over five years. Celanese was the only participant in what Herbert had hoped would be a program of industrial sponsorship, at $200,000 per year, by which leading chemical companies would support unrestricted basic research in the Dreyfus Laboratory. Visits to Dow, du Pont, Carbide, and others soon convinced him that he'd been idealistic, not to say naive, in believing that they would underwrite research in a laboratory named for the founder of a major competitor.

The Dreyfus/RTI agreement provided for well-defined investigations to develop fundamental knowledge with a supplemental sponsorship that went beyond the sustaining Dreyfus Foundation grant. Under these terms, CDL performed research in the public domain for the U.S. Department of Agriculture, NASA, Atomic Energy Commission, Army and Air Force research and materiel commands, U.S. Office of Saline Water, National Institutes of Health, Cotton Producers Institute, the N.C. Textile Manufacturers Association, and others.

The Dreyfus Foundation's decision not to continue the grant beyond the initial ten years found RTI prepared. First, the trustees generously acceded to a proposal for $400,000 in additional funding over the four years remaining until Peterlin's retirement in 1973 at the then-mandatory age of 65.

Second, CDL operating policies were relaxed and re-directed. Emphasis shifted, during the four-year period, from exclusively fundamental studies related to pure property investigations and the synthesis and modification of polymer structures, toward applications-oriented projects that would contribute more directly to the polymer technology needs of industry and government.

Examples were Ingram's transmission and scanning electron microscopy studies of the physical stresses to which cotton fibers are subjected during manufacturing processes and the fabrication of finished materials, and on the adaptability of fabrics to treatment with durable press agents. Others were

Schindler's work on charge mosaic membranes for seawater desalination and, later, on designing adsorbent polyimides to capture toxic impurities in ambient air. Applied polymer research also included research on anticorrosion and antiabrasion coatings, adhesives, and flame and heat-resistant treatments.

Despite best efforts, the transition from basic to applied emphasis met with obstacles and less than hoped-for success. For one thing, the intellectual endowments that led Peterlin to mastery of the concepts and designs of fundamental science were not readily adaptable to the challenges of leadership in applied science. For another, although several CDL staff members demonstrated later on their talents for salesmanship, none of them then had, nor had they needed, more than the slightest exposure to cultivating a client or to writing a proposal that would outshine the competition's.

Through the quality of their studies and unrestricted publication, CDL scientists had more than met the objective of creating a new center for fundamental polymer research. Recognition within the international polymer science community had long since become a given. A great deal of this regard was due to Peterlin himself, partly because of his position as head of the laboratory, mostly because of his original and sustained contributions to basic knowledge. He had brought to RTI an illustrious, 30-year research and teaching career that made him one of Europe's preeminent polymer scientists. During his 12 RTI years that reputation, and the Institute's as well, had been burnished and expanded to worldwide dimensions by his scores of published papers, invited lectures, editorships, medals, and other professional awards.

Nevertheless, the decline in CDL's contract revenues continued after Peterlin retired at the end of October 1973.

After struggling with the problem for two years, Herbert and vice president Monroe E. Wall decided that CDL scientists' resources for, and interest in, developing specialized polymer materials for medical and health applications would blend readily with the medicinal-related research that had been growing for 15 years in Wall's chemistry and life sciences (CLS) centers. Accordingly, a polymer research laboratory, incorporating CDL staff and programs, was folded into CLS under physical sciences research director Colin G. Pitt.

Schindler and others had already been collaborating with Pitt's division on development of a biodegradable polymer capsule for the sustained release of hormonal substances, contraceptive drugs in particular. The capsule is an inch-long tube about the diameter of a pencil lead. Implanted by injection into a woman's hip or upper arm, its contents slowly diffuse into the bloodstream at a steady, predetermined rate that avoids the fluctuating efficacy levels that are inherent with oral or injected dosages. It also eliminates a woman's need to remember her daily pill or to use another form of contraception.

After the implant's contents are fully released, which can take up to a year or longer, it gradually biodegrades and is eliminated from the body without surgery.

Named Capronor^tm^, and patented in 1979, this drug delivery system is a potentially significant contribution to an improved quality of life for much of the world's population. It endures as the topic of many scientific papers and for more than 15 years has deservedly been a top newsmaker for RTI.

Capronor^tm^ has undergone extensive testing for safety and potency. Preclinical trials were conducted by the Duke University Medical Center, Phase I trials by Southern Research Institute, and Phase II trials by the University of California at San Francisco. Under auspices of the World Health Organization, RTI's biostructure (the capsule) and the antifertility drug have also been tested in England, India, Indonesia, and Italy.

A successor design is expected to have longer shelf life and an even more stable release rate. Further refinement and testing are proceeding under a three-year National Institutes of Health contract that began early in 1989.

Ingram's interests in using electron microscopy to study the morphology of biological tissues and cells also date from the early 1970s. With funding from NIH through the Duke University Medical Center, where he is an adjunct member of the pathology faculty, he is in the final year of a five-year study of structure function correlation in the atrium of the heart.

In the spring of 1989 a McGraw-Hill subsidiary published a landmark work entitled *Microprobe Analysis in Medicine*, coauthored by Ingram and John D. Shelburne, M.D., of Duke. Written for physicians, the book is the first text dealing with the diagnostic applications of microprobe analysis, a technique that provides clinical pathologists with microstructural and chemical information that cannot, at present, be obtained in any other way.

Ingram foresees rich rewards in research on microstructures as the essential link between biomedicine and biomaterials, fields in which his colleagues at Duke and N.C. State University are renowned.

Another form of health-related polymer research deals not with humans, but with threats to the lives of sea birds and aquatic mammals. The thousands of tons of plastic trash annually dumped or lost in the world's oceans are estimated to kill, by strangulation, entanglement, and suffocation, more than a million birds and 100,000 mammals every year. In projects for the Navy, Department of Commerce, and private clients, RTI is measuring the lifetime of plastics in water, and investigating biodegradable and photodegradable enhancements for polymer products.

With Pitt's resignation in the fall of 1987, after nearly 24 years at RTI, vice president C. Edgar Cook asked Monroe Wall to take interim responsibility for a newly designated Polymer Sciences Department. (Wall had relinquished his vice president's title in 1983 to return to full-time research as chief scientist.) The following summer, Cook and Wall produced a master stroke by enticing Vivian Stannett back to RTI with yet another Camille Dreyfus tie. As the Institute's Camille Dreyfus Scientist, he began to chart the future of a polymer research program that he had helped to establish 27 years earlier.

8. SOME SECOND-YEAR FIRSTS

Hugh Hunter's airplane ride to Philadelphia proved to be a key 1960 event for RTI.

Early in the year Duke clinicians had advised him and Herbert about applied research possibilities in cancer chemotherapy under sponsorship of the National Institutes of Health (NIH). A priority for additional laboratory activity to balance desk-type research had been part of the RTI equation for nearly two years, so when Marcus Hobbs, Duke chemistry professor and at that time dean of the university, confirmed at an Executive Committee meeting in March that a chemical synthesis program would be a valuable adjunct to university clinical research, RTI decided to go after it.

With NIH encouragement, the right man for cultivating this opportunity to fullest advantage surfaced in the person of Monroe E. Wall. Hunter visited him in Philadelphia, found his credentials to be all that the NIH had portrayed them to be, and returned to RTI to present them to Herbert and the committee.

The airplane ride was significant because if Hunter wasn't the only prospective employer interested in Wall, he was the first one who bothered to make the trip.

Wall's availability came about through more of the timely twists favoring RTI. In 1960 he was head, as he had been for ten years, of the plant steroid section at the U.S. Department of Agriculture's Eastern Regional Research Laboratory, where he had received a USDA award for superior individual accomplishment and his section a similar group award. Many more scientific honors have come his way during 29 years, so far, at RTI. He had joined the USDA 19 years earlier, soon after receiving a Ph.D. in agricultural chemistry at Rutgers University.

The timely twists involved territorial differences both within the USDA and between the USDA and the National Cancer Institute (NCI). With plant samples coming from all over the world, Wall's laboratory had conducted extensive screening efforts in a search for chemical substances that could be converted to cortisone, a steroid best known for its use in arthritis treatment. In 1959 the USDA terminated its program of screening for cortisone precursors; Wall saw the emphasis in his section being redirected to oils and fatty acids.

Concurrently, the NCI, eager to expand its own screening of natural products for antitumor properties, desired access to Wall's thousands of plant extracts. The USDA failed to cooperate, even though Wall had, just a year or two earlier, supplied about a thousand samples to the NCI's Cancer Chemotherapy National Service Center (CCNSC).

At this point, an NIH official who knew of Wall's disappointment said to him, in essence, leave government, we'll give you support under contract. He further volunteered to spread the word around. It reached RTI, among other institutions, and soon afterwards Hunter bought his airline ticket.

As it has to other high achievers, the RTI proposition looked good to Wall. There was space at Bacon Street, an N.C. General Assembly line-item equipment appropriation of $200,000 had been voted, the NCI's commitment was in hand, and RTI's university associations were promising. Hunter had given assurances that "Monroe could do the kind of work he wanted to do," and Herbert that a chemistry research program was his to build. In May, Wall accepted the appointment as director of RTI's new Natural Products Laboratory.

Wall's scientific accomplishments and standing were all that anyone could ask. Also standing him in good stead was his experience at the USDA in writing proposals (such as the one for screening plants for cortisone precursors). Although the NCI had pledged contract awards to Wall and his new employer, he still had to prepare written proposals setting forth acceptable research goals, methods, staffing, and cost. Wall's proposal success rate, both early and late, may well be RTI's best (although he now willingly concedes that laurel to associates F. Ivy Carroll and Ed Cook.)

His first two winners were to the NCI's CCNSC, as planned. One, which has been in renewal or extension almost without interruption ever since, was to screen plant samples for tumor-inhibiting substances. It called for the extraction, isolation, and purification of chemical constituents that would be tested by other NCI contractors for cancer chemotherapeutic value. Those showing promise would come back to RTI for further purification and/or modification of the natural product, and the synthesis of chemical analogs.

The second Natural Products Laboratory (NPL) proposal to the CCSNC, another which held long-term implications for further, related research, dealt with the preparation of novel steroid hormone analogs for testing as hormonal, antihormonal, and anticarcinogenic agents.

As good as its word, the NCI fully redeemed its pledges by funding the RTI proposals, as it continues to do, but there was a long six-month delay before formal acceptance.

A taxicab meter was one thing running in RTI's favor during this waiting period, and NPL staffing was another. Wall's first recruits were former USDA colleagues Samuel G. Levine, who left four years later to join the N.C. State faculty, and Charles S. Fenske, who remained as a research chemist and the laboratory's business and support services manager until his death in 1983.

Next were "two of the best Ph.D. chemists UNC ever graduated," as Wall describes them. Since coming from Chapel Hill to RTI in December 1960, Ivy Carroll has won a national reputation, particularly for his use of molecular modeling techniques in designing compounds for biological applications such as analgesics, depressants, stimulants, hallucinogens, and antiradiation, antiparasitic, antifertility, and anticancer agents. Since 1975 Carroll has been director of organic and medicinal chemistry research.

At that same time, the end of 1960, Wall committed a position to Ed Cook, the appointment to take effect after Cook's year as a postdoctoral fellow in England at Cambridge University. The wide professional recognition Cook enjoys is based on his research in steroid and flavonoid synthesis, drug metabolism, antifertility compounds, and immunoassay development. He was named director of bioorganic chemistry in 1975 and became RTI vice president for chemistry and life sciences in 1983, when Wall gave up that position's management responsibilities in favor of the chief scientist title.

As for taxicabs, they weren't all that plentiful at the NIH complex in Bethesda, Maryland, on a late summer's afternoon in 1960. Wall found himself opening the door on one side of a taxi while two would-be passengers were doing the same on the other side. Since the Washington airport was their common destination, they agreed to share the cab. Wall's companions turned out to be with the U.S. Army's Walter Reed Hospital, now Medical Center, and they had a problem. After learning a bit about Wall's background, they described it. He responded that they might be talking to just the right person.

And so, in as unlikely a circumstance as anyone could fail to foresee, they were. Wall's subsequent proposal for preparing antiradiation compounds started a 29-year association between Walter Reed and RTI that has included, among other subjects, continuing radiosynthesis research, development of antimalarials, and the synthesis of controlled drugs. In view of the delay at CCNSC, that first proposal acceptance was also a personal relief, for although Wall knew NCI support would be forthcoming, and had felt no pressure from Herbert and Hunter, he knew well enough that "this is a sink or swim business" and was glad to have the contract.

Other unlikely circumstances materially affected the Natural Products Laboratory in another way and will be recounted in a minute, but more was going on at RTI in 1960 than chemistry alone.

Second-year firsts occurred on several research and organizational fronts. Among them, Gertrude Cox took early retirement from State College to join RTI full-time on July 1.

By then the Statistics Research Division (SRD) staff had grown to 22 and a variety of contract subjects, and she and Al Finkner had already effected a first, RTI's first intradiscipline subdivision, a process that has gone on and on and on throughout all RTI research areas. Finkner was head of sampling research, Hale C. Sweeny of industrial statistics, and William S. Connor of experimental design and engineering. During his nearly five years at RTI, Connor's section was responsible for gearing up an innovative program in basic and applied research on engineering reliability. Early clients included the Office of Ordnance Research, other Army R&D commands on subsystem component malfunction probability, and a Bell Telephone Laboratories contract on statistical methods for evaluating the reliability of complex electronic systems, specifically those of the Nike missile.

In addition to heading statistical research on technical operating problems and industrial processes, Sweeny had special responsibilities for SRD, and RTI, program development and promotional activities. He stayed at RTI long enough to get his ten-year pin before moving down Cornwallis Road to the Burroughs Wellcome Co.

Finkner was probably neither his own nor Cox's preference for head of the sampling section. Their choice might well have been Daniel G. Horvitz, an Iowa State College Ph.D. and Red Sox fan who had been their colleague at N.C. State before leaving to become statistics director with a Philadelphia market research firm. He was unavailable in 1960, however, having accepted, from the University of Chicago, a two-year Ford Foundation appointment that took him to Burma as senior adviser on a teaching program in statistics and agricultural economics at the University of Rangoon. It wasn't until 1962 that Horvitz could begin an RTI career during which his distinctive contributions to the statistical sciences put him right up there alongside Cox and Finkner.*

Changes in title, though not in duties, occurred in June when the board elected RTI's first vice presidents. They were Sam Ashton, VP for business and facilities, who also retained his positions as treasurer and corporate secretary, and Hunter, VP for all research operations except those in statistics. As deans and even chancellors knew, Cox had a distaste for intermediaries between herself and the top. She would report to Herbert.

The search for a new Operational Sciences Laboratory director ended on October 1st with the arrival from Washington of Edgar A. Parsons. He and

* All three were elected by their peers as Fellows of the American Statistical Association, an honor bestowed upon fewer than five percent of the ASA's membership. Later on, so were chief scientist B. V. Shah, statistics vice president James R. Chromy, and biometrics vice president W. Kenneth Poole.

Hunter achieved a first almost at once by changing the laboratory's name, another process that has gone on and on and on throughout all RTI research areas. The term operational sciences had been coined the previous year as an all-purpose combination to convey capabilities in the distinct fields of operations research and management science. About all it conveyed was confusion, however, so it was renamed the Operations Research Division. Four years later another change seemed appropriate and it became the Operations Research and Economics Division. This name stuck until 1971, when the division disappeared entirely.

Bud Parsons brought new ideas about resource management, systems analysis, command and control, information theory, and other subjects, none of them delivering more fruitful results than civil defense research, as related in Chapter 12. This was Parsons' field of expertise. An economics Ph.D. from Cornell, he came to RTI after six years with the Office of Civil Defense and Mobilization, where he had been chief of economics research and deputy chief of operations research. Parsons' 100 months at RTI also saw advances in computer science and health research, and the start of a modest program in regional economic development. When he resigned at the beginning of 1970 the division had grown from a staff of 6 to 94, making it the Institute's largest at that time.

Two other 1960 firsts were of a business nature. In August, board chairman Watts Hill reported at the annual meeting that the Research Triangle Foundation's loans to RTI, then totaling $319,438.11, had been converted by the Foundation to a gift, "said gift being in accordance with the Foundation's chartered objective to support the development of research activities," as well as in accordance with principles agreed upon in 1958. (See Chapter 11.)

In October the Foundation transferred title of 16.29 acres to RTI as the site for the Camille Dreyfus Laboratory. The parcel was valued at $4,242.56, or $260 per acre, a figure that must shiver the timbers of later investors in office and industrial developments on the Park's periphery.

On December 16 the Robert M. Hanes Memorial Building was dedicated, and on December 31 and January 1 RTI and the Foundation moved in.

Returning to Natural Products Laboratory affairs, the *Camptotheca acuminata* tree frames a succession of unlikely circumstances and ironies that date back to 1933, when an American botanist in south central China forwarded a handful of its seeds to the USDA. Fortunately, he labeled them simply as "No. 75. Collected on a rocky slope in Chang An, Yung Hsien." From then on to 1960 and beyond, the anonymous "No. 75" has refuted Robert Louis Stevenson's melancholy complaint, made in 1881, that "Science writes of the world as if with the cold finger of a starfish."

Camptotheca acuminata was known to the USDA as a botanical rarity, the only member of the plant family Nyssaceae, that had already been introduced to the United States, thought of in terms of possible use as a shade tree for the nursery trade. It was not successful for that purpose. Most of the trees were discarded, and the few survivors were given only casual attention as curiosities.

Identified by number and not by name, however, the seeds from China were planted soon after their arrival at the USDA Plant Introduction Station in Glenn Dale, Maryland. Later, most were sent to the station at Chico, California, where two small trees survived. Unobtrusive specimens of no evident value, they remained undisturbed only because the space they occupied wasn't needed for other plantings.

Nearly twenty years later, a chemical extract from *C. acuminata* was routinely included among thousands of plant samples being examined for properties as cortisone precursors. The extracts were tested in Monroe Wall's Philadelphia plant steroid laboratory. Giving a negative result for cortisone purposes the *C. acuminata* sample was consigned to a storage shelf. There the unprepossessing extract rested all but forgotten for nearly six years until accident gave it another chance.

Wall and his administrative counterpart, J. J. Willaman, had realized from the start of the cortisone precursor search that the thousands of botanical samples arriving from all over the world offered an unparalleled opportunity for chemical and biological examination of wild plants for potentially valuable constituents. They proceeded to examine thousands of extracts for alkaloids, flavonoids, and tannins, and for antibiotic, antiviral and antitumor activity.

In 1957 NCI's CCNSC requested 1,000 extracts for antitumor testing. Wall and Willaman supplied them from off-the-shelf, including one prepared from the leaves of *Camptotheca acuminata*.

By 1959 the results were in. From the thousand extracts, only ten showed any promise against the tumor that was being tested. *C. acuminata* was among them, but once again it seemed destined for oblivion when changes at the USDA resulted in Willaman's retirement and in Wall's reassignment and his departure for RTI in 1960.

Screening plants for antitumor activity was the subject of RTI's first proposal to and contract with the National Cancer Institute and Wall, still alert to *C. acuminata's* possibilities, promptly sent for new samples of twigs and leaves from the trees at Chico. Extracts from these samples proved to be inactive, but by September of 1961 extracts from *Camptotheca acuminata* fruit showed activity that was well above the marginal level in a highly selective leukemia test. With this encouragement, extract samples were prepared from twigs, bark, and wood.

Once more the tree survived a possible rebuff, for extracts from bark and wood showed the same activity found in the original extract from leaves and from the later fruit sample. *C. acuminata's* yield of leaves and fruit is low, and isolating chemical constituents from them was complicated by the high content of chlorophyll and other unwanted coloring matter in the leaves, and by the large number of oils in the fruit. Future research would have had doubtful value unless the active constituent was found in the more plentiful, woody parts of the tree.

Fortuitous circumstance had once again sided with *Camptotheca acuminata*.

In March 1965, after months of laborious and painstaking laboratory operations, the RTI research team succeeded in isolating a tiny quantity of a pure crystalline substance that reproduced the antitumor activity of the earlier, cruder extracts.

Naming the new substance camptothecin, Wall, Cook, Keith H. Palmer, and M. C. Wani reported to CCNSC that it yielded a high degree of reproducible potency against mouse leukemia L-1210. Biological assays at CCNSC confirmed the findings.

Disclosure of the isolation and structure elucidation of camptothecin was made in an RTI paper given by Wall at the June 1966 annual meeting of the International Union for Pure and Applied Chemistry. Accounts also appeared in American Chemical Society and USDA publications and in the daily press.

The question of future supply was now critical. By themselves, the two trees in Chico couldn't come close to providing adequate quantities of material for experimental purposes unless they were removed and totally used up. But destruction of the two trees was unthinkable. The interior of mainland China had long been closed to the U.S. and was no longer available as a source. No one knew where other specimens might be obtained to provide propagating seed material. The USDA began a systematic search of the West Coast for any that might remain. Thirteen were located in California and eight in Taiwan.

A horticulturist at Chico, meanwhile, succeeded in germinating seed from the 1963 crop of *C. acuminata* fruit, and several hundred seedlings were planted out the following spring. They grew rapidly and were about 18 inches high in August 1964.

But the supply question was by no means resolved. It became of paramount importance to find out if the active constituent was present in such young plants. If it was necessary to wait five or ten years for them to reach maturity, laboratory research and testing would be agonizingly delayed.

Some seedlings from the new crop were removed and tested. They were active. This made it clear that the camptothecin compound would be available in working quantities. Working quantities, but hardly abundance, for in the case of *C. acuminata* the average ratio, by weight, of extract to original sample was about 1 to 20,000. "Was" is the proper verb form, for synthesis of the compound lay ahead.

The once-unheeded Sample No. 75 leapt to national prominence in the spring of 1970 when the National Institutes of Health announced that camptothecin "stands front stage center" in the search for drugs against cancers of the colon and rectum.

Stressing the preliminary nature of the findings, NIH reported that in the National Cancer Institute's first clinical trials to test camptothecin dosage limits, the drug was administered to a group of adults suffering from various types of advanced cancers that were no longer responding to conventional treatment. All but one case in 17 yielded objective evidence of tumor regression. Durations of response were brief, five months was the longest, but were useful to the patients both in weight gain and increase in a sense of well-being.

Toxic side effects were described as generally manageable. Later trials could not confirm this finding, unfortunately. Still that early announcement was a cause for elation at RTI. The NIH had already intensified its searches for *C. acuminata* trees in California and for synthetic routes to camptothecin analogs in laboratories at RTI and elsewhere. Both merit a few more paragraphs.

The 13 trees that had been found in Southern California provided enough material for plantings of several thousand seeds which would assure a sufficient supply, in the future, for research and experimental treatment programs. But the NIH wanted older and bigger trees that could more quickly yield greater quantities of raw material for the extraction process.

Area newspapers and broadcast media cooperated with the NIH in a publicity campaign about *C. acuminata's* potential medical value. Within just a few days the USDA's Chico station and the Los Angeles arboretum were swamped with specimens. They were mostly avocado, whose leaf closely resembles *C. acuminata's*, with a scattering of fig, magnolia, viburnum, and ivy. The NIH and news media then urged the public *not* to send in more samples.

One sample sent by a Beverly Hills resident was from what a USDA official described as a "superb" tree that was well worth all the trouble. Its owner had liked it because it hid a telephone pole in the back yard. Chinese farmers were known to use their trees for firewood and for hanging bundles of rice on the lower branches to dry. Even more worthwhile purposes may still—one day, some day—be served by the unheralded seed sample No. 75 that started a series of chemical and medical investigations which showed such bright promise.

Despite the ultimately disappointing results of those first clinical tests, interest in the novel alkaloid did not lapse, but merely languished at a lower level of effort. Under NIH sponsorship RTI continues what is now more than twenty years of research on synthesizing analogs of the compound in pure form for further study as tumor inhibitors. Wall and Wani continue to publish and lecture on the subject, even though it is now but a small part of RTI chemistry and life sciences programs that include major activities in chemical, biochemical, organic synthesis, and pharmacological research.

Camptothecin began a comeback in the late 1980s with the discovery that it uniquely inhibits the activity of an enzyme called topoisomerase I. Topo I complexes with DNA, and in this form of DNA normal cell division occurs. In the presence of camptothecin in very low concentration, Topo I is inhibited and cell division cannot occur. Since tumor cells divide more rapidly than normal cells, the tumor cells are killed. No other cancer chemotherapeutic compound has such potency; a few others are weakly active. RTI researchers have, by total synthesis, prepared a number of analogs which are 10 to 20 times more potent than camptothecin.

Taxol has a history somewhat similar to and every bit as dramatic as camptothecin's. Isolated from the bark of *Taxus brevifolia*, a species of yew tree, the compound was reported in a 1971 RTI paper to show high experimental activity against a number of animal leukemia and solid tumor cells. Extraction of the compound in its natural state yielded uneconomically small amounts, however, and its complex structure thwarted efforts at synthesis. RTI researchers turned to other natural products.

Scientists at the Albert Einstein Medical College discovered in 1979 that taxol specifically and reversibly binds to tubulin, a protein that's important in cell division. Taxol is the only plant product known to promote the assembly of microtubules and to inhibit tubulin disassembly. This unique mechanism of action makes it the prototype of a new class of cancer chemotherapeutic agents.

The finding revived National Cancer Institute interest, and taxol became the topic of an NCI poster session at a 1988 meeting of the American Society of Pharmacognosy. Wall, an ASP honorary life member, was there and returned to tell his RTI colleagues that "To my surprise and great pleasure, I learned that oncologists who are working with taxol regard it as one of the best new anticancer agents they have seen in many years."

LATE FLASH!

On November 24, 1989, *Science* magazine published a paper reporting that 9-amino-20(RS)-camptothecin, one of the camptothecin analogs synthesized at RTI, caused total tumor regression and long-term, disease-free survival of immunodeficient mice carrying human colon cancer cell lines. The general toxicity of the treatments was low and allowed for repeated courses of therapy.

Based on experiments conducted by the Stehlin Foundation at St. Joseph Hospital in Houston, the paper was written by scientists there, by RTI's Wall and Wani, and by investigators at the Johns Hopkins University School of Medicine and the New York University School of Medicine.

Colorectal cancer is the third most common malignancy in the United States, with approximately 147,000 new cases diagnosed every year. It accounts for 60,000 deaths annually, about 12 percent of all cancer deaths.

"In 20 years of experimenting with human colon cancers, we have never seen this type of dramatic response with other anticancer drugs," said John Stehlin, scientific director of the Stehlin Foundation.

Said John Silber of NYU, "The striking effectiveness of these drugs makes their further study absolutely essential, with the ultimate aim of bringing them to clinical trial."

Fifty-six years after being collected from a rocky hill in a remote Chinese province, those seeds from the *Camptotheca acuminata* are perhaps on their way to becoming an important part of medical history. A key development of 1989-90 is reported in Chapter 15.

Meanwhile, and again poaching a bit into 1990, taxol has been found to give complete and partial remissions to ovarian cancer patients whose tumors had become resistant to all standard chemotherapeutic agents. Favorable results of Phase One and Phase Two clinical trials were reported in June by oncologists from the Albert Einstein and Johns Hopkins medical schools. Phase Three clinical trials have been slated, and the NCI will fund basic research to increase the yield of taxol from the *Taxus brevifolia's* bark by biotechnology procedures such as cell culture.

9. Earlier: The Process Begins

"Our history must needs retrograde for the space of a few pages to inform the reader of certain passages material to his understanding of the rest of this important narrative."
Ivanhoe, by Sir Walter Scott

At the beginning of 1990 the Research Triangle Park's 6,700 acres contain research operations of 54 corporate, academic, and government occupants whose payrolls include over 32,000 employees. They occupy more than 12 million square feet of laboratories and offices which represent brick and mortar investment in excess of two billion dollars.

High-tech has come to be perceived as the magical "Open, Sesame" to regional economic development and prosperity. States, cities, and university communities all across America pin their hopes for industrial growth on the ability to attract high technology research, development, and manufacturing activities.

Unlike Ali Baba's incantation in Scheherezade's tale, however, the pronouncement of a high-tech initiative cannot alone produce instant regional riches. Even North Carolina's Research Triangle Park, the world's most successful R&D center, required years to attain critical mass.

"The Park can afford to be choosy now, but those early years* were tough on all of us," University of North Carolina president William Friday told the *Carolina Alumni News* for quotation in its issue of June 1983.

"The whole enterprise was held together with bailing (sic) wire and adhesive tape, and you always had to be looking over your shoulder hoping nothing was behind you, because there wasn't a spare nickel in the budget, and hardly enough to keep the whole thing going.

"Today it represents the finest example I know of cooperation between the corporate, government, and higher education communities. But the most incredible thing about it is that it exists at all. When it started, all the elements

* This chapter sketches some key events of those early years. A detailed account of Research Triangle Park funding, land transactions, zoning, and corporate development must await the full-scale review that only the Research Triangle Foundation can perform.

were there for total destruction. You couldn't put together a more violent mixture if you tried.

"There was a tangible jealousy among the various layers of government involved, no such thing as a Triangle identity like we have now. There was a very real animosity between government and industry. There was no basis to predict that industry and higher education could not only get along, but work together for the benefit of both. There was no history of the three universities cooperating on the scale it would require for the Park to succeed.

"If you had any sense you wouldn't even have tried to make it work. And yet somehow it did. I think a vision came to them all at the same time that they were part of something unique, that could work, and everything began to fall into place."

George Simpson calls what happened a "process." He is the individual who, more than any other, side-stepped total destruction, diluted the violent mixture, transmuted jealousy into harmony, cultivated the seeds of cooperation and, as he put it, "tried hard to avoid problems and keep the process going" until everything began to fall into place. He had lots of help from lots of people who saw "all at the same time that they were part of something unique, that could work . . . ."

"It was all a process," emphasis on the process, Simpson recalls of his more than two years of total immersion that began on September 25, 1956, with his appointment as executive director of the Research Triangle Committee, Inc.

The process was not one of discovery like Balboa upon a peak in Darien, or Archimedes displacing water in his bathtub, or James W. Marshall spotting a glint of gold in the tail-race of the sawmill at Sutter's Fort. Yet in their way the regional, scientific, and economic products of the Research Triangle's process were not dissimilar to the consequences of those other great events.

Rather than any sudden revelation, the process as Simpson has described it was permeative, diffuse. Its goal of industrial growth based on university scientific research resources was clear, but distant. There was no known path, no precedent. No one had been there. In the process prudently followed by Simpson and his governing committees, recommendations for action were preceded by the assembly of exhaustive information about those university resources, and by the analysis of data and opinion obtained from scientists and corporate executives about the regional characteristics that were attractive to businesses seeking new laboratory sites.

"Before 1952" is the earliest that anyone has come to fixing a date that first links Romeo H. Guest of Greensboro with the general notion that scientific research resources could be a promotional plus in luring industry to North

Carolina. By 1954 Guest was actively promoting and had prepared the mock-up of a brochure, entitled "Conditioned for Research—North Carolina's Own Research Triangle," that he would print and mail to businesses across the nation.

Guest was an industrial construction company executive in search of customers. A graduate of and visitor to MIT, he was scarcely alone in being impressed by the high-tech corporate expansions and successful technology-based ventures along Route 128 and elsewhere in the Boston-Cambridge area. The developments were routinely attributed to the go-getting R&D environment fueled by MIT, Harvard, and the region's other universities. A similar situation existed on the West Coast around Stanford University.

Predominantly rural North Carolina was no match for cosmopolitan centers such as Boston and the San Francisco Bay Area, but Guest wondered if UNC, Duke, and N.C. State couldn't offer inducements of a like nature, positive R&D attractions that could help lure advanced manufacturers' investment.

Such companies were bypassing the state. North Carolina's nonfarm employment remained concentrated in the traditional industries of textiles, furniture, cigarettes, paper, which could not support substantial new investment. Per capita income levels steadily fell further below national averages. Tax revenues were insufficient to provide desired improvements in schools and other public services. The state was being denied a future of economic opportunity, development, and growth.

Perhaps most serious of all, too many young men and women, especially those with college degrees, were leaving the state to find satisfying careers elsewhere. Census data frequently cited by Herbert showed that in 1950 native Tarheels living in other states exceeded 20 percent of North Carolina's population. For a speech in May 1958, Governor Hodges wrote that "two-thirds of these young people trained in science at these three institutions are forced to leave North Carolina, and indeed the entire South, to find suitable employment."

Guest was well acquainted with the state's industry hunters and found them to be receptive listeners. Among them were Brandon Hodges and Walter W. Harper, both of whom agreed with his broadly stated thesis of the universities as a core for research activities that would be a magnet for technology-based industry. The idea that industrial advance is linked to university research was not invented in North Carolina, of course, but the state has capitalized on it with singular success, thanks primarily to the coincidence that clustered three research universities so close together. It had to be coincidence, for no one would have planned it that way.

Proximity to any of the campuses was the promotional theme initially struck by Guest, Harper, and Brandon Hodges. Following a 1953 visit to the E.R. Squibb pharmaceuticals firm, Guest wrote to the company in June urging the location of a facility near Chapel Hill, where "research chemists will be happy." A July letter stated his hope that Squibb was still considering "our research area at Durham, Chapel Hill, and Raleigh."

The points of a research triangle had been identified.

Capital letters were added three months later, on October 10, 1953, when Guest made a list of topics to discuss with Brandon Hodges and wrote "Research Triangle—Celanese." This diary notation is reported by Mary Virginia Currie Jones in *A Golden Triangle of Research: Romeo Holland Guest—His Conception of and Involvement in the Development of the Research Triangle Park*, her UNC Master of Arts thesis written in 1978. Another citation dates the christening as June 1, 1954. This is given in William B. Hamilton's paper entitled "The Research Triangle of North Carolina: A Study in Leadership for the Common Weal" and published in *The South Atlantic Quarterly* issue for spring 1966. If Jones's date hadn't been documented, a more appealing version would be the one attributed to Guest himself by the *Durham Morning Herald*. On April 26, 1981, the paper quoted him as having said that "It was ten a.m. on Dec. 31, 1954. I was with Gov. Hodges and I looked at a map and noticed that the universities formed a triangle."

Whenever and wherever the name Research Triangle first appeared, the idea of a research center was taking hold within a widening circle of observers who viewed it favorably. This was particularly the case at State College, where Guest was a director of both the Textile Foundation and the Engineering Foundation. Quick and approving responses came from the chancellor, Carey H. Bostian, from School of Textiles dean Malcolm E. Campbell, engineering dean J. Harold Lampe, and from William A. Newell, director of the Textile Research Center.

Lt. Gov. Luther Hodges succeeded to the Governor's office on November 7, 1954, following the death of Gov. William B. Umstead. He was probably somewhat familiar with Guest's research center notions, but heard about them in detail on December 1st from Bostian, Campbell, Lampe, and Brandon Hodges. According to Jones's account, "Bostian did not feel that Luther Hodges exhibited much enthusiasm for the concept at that meeting although he did request that the North Carolina State people continue to evaluate it."

Possibly that was so, although Hodges himself wrote that "immediately I saw the potential it held . . . ." Either way, the force and extent of his enthusiasm weren't in doubt for long. His leadership, his incredible drive, and his constancy to the program were critical to the achievement that lay ahead. The Research Triangle idea was made to order for the governor who would entitle his memoirs *Businessman in the State House*, and whose administration's main thrust would be industrial diversification and expansion. Hodges jumped on it.

On January 27, 1955, Bostian gave him *A Proposal for the Development of an Industrial Research Center in North Carolina*, by the textile school's Campbell and Newell. "Written some time after midnight," as Newell recalled in a letter to Herbert, the 10-page proposal neglected to mention the Research Triangle name, but was a prescient document in other respects. With generous references to the Duke and Carolina campuses as well as their own, the authors made their case simply: "Unquestionably, industry, especially in recent years, has stepped up its research efforts. But it is equally clear that research and educational facilities and the existence of other research organizations in a given area can attract and develop industry."

Campbell and Newell can be awarded a first for their statement that "Specific plans should be made for the development of an area between Raleigh, Durham and Chapel Hill and near Raleigh-Durham Airport, as a center for industrial research."

They not only specified a "where" for the center, they also called for enlisting the participation of all three universities, for a survey of research facilities and faculty resources at the campuses, and for publicizing these and the other regional advantages that would "encourage establishment of industrial research laboratories in the area."

Hodges wasted no time. On February 9, 1955, he met for luncheon at the Governor's Mansion with UNC president Gordon Gray, Duke vice president Paul Gross, and the State College people.

During this luncheon Gross declared his conviction that plans should include a contract research institute, an opinion he had stated in an earlier conversation with Guest. He felt strongly about it. Simpson remembers a later meeting at which an item of business was the proposed half-million-dollar allocation to underwrite the universities' research institute. There was some demurral about releasing such a sum to university control until Gross made it clear that if there wasn't to be an institute Duke wouldn't participate further. As Simpson recounted the incident to Herbert, Hodges looked around at the others in the room, as if silently counting votes, before replying that there'd be one.

Gray was preconditioned to receive hospitably Hodges' optimism about the nascent Research Triangle. By coincidence, consultants assessing UNC's physics department had written, without knowledge of others' activities, that "Rather than competing adversely with each other, they (meaning the universities) should add to and enhance the opportunity for development of a major scientific and industrial community."

Within weeks of his first meeting with the Triangle university representatives, Hodges' unflagging verve was beginning to push the Research Triangle idea in every possible public forum. As Herbert commented later, "Although nothing was happening in the scrub pine that would become the Research Triangle Park, and committee meetings were the only mark of progress, salesman Hodges was selling his Research Triangle, and he would never stop."

A short digression will underscore the founders' success in generating a statewide feeling of participation, even proprietorship, in the Research Triangle. Over the years Herbert and others traveled the state to give RTI and Research Triangle Park progress reports at any number of civic, professional, and business gatherings. On many of these occasions they met with almost identical occurrences. After the talk or program at least one member of the audience would approach, saying something akin to "You know I (or, increasingly, my father) was one of the first people that Luther Hodges (or Romeo Guest, or Bob Hanes) talked to about the Research Triangle." The circumstances of that remembered conversation, whether a small meeting or a large convention, don't matter. Neither does when it took place. What matters is the priceless sense of identification.

Hodges' prominent role in Research Triangle affairs is one reason that has led some visitors, reporters, and even some state and university officials to assume that state funding launched the Research Triangle. A second reason is their disbelief that it could have been developed without state subsidy. But it was. Hodges gave prodigiously of his vigor, time, and leadership, yet the Research Triangle was not intended to be and never was a state enterprise, not a dime of state money underwrote its formation. (An existing state policy called for the N.C. Highway Department to construct all-weather access roads to any new industrial facilities. By August 1958 Hodges had authorized $150,000 for roadways within the RTPark.)

The need for an organizational structure had been anticipated by Guest, Harper, and others, so in the spring of 1955 Hodges formed a Governor's Research Triangle Development Council, with himself as a member and Hanes as chairman.

Other council members were Armstrong of Celanese in Charlotte; president A. Hollis Edens of Duke; E.Y. Floyd, director of the N.C. Plant Food Institute in Raleigh; UNC's Gray; Brandon Hodges; H. Grady Rankin, an attorney in Gastonia and president of Superior Mills there; C.W. Reynolds of the Western Electric Company in Winston-Salem; and William H. Ruffin, president of Erwin Mills in Durham.

The council was buttressed by a Working Committee, appointed in June. Lampe of State College was chairman of this all-university group. Its other members were: from UNC, Gordon W. Blackwell, chairman of the Institute of Research in Social Science, Henry T. Clark, Division of Health Affairs administrator, and School of Business Administration dean R.J.M. Hobbs, who retired and was replaced by Arthur Roe, director of UNC's Institute of Natural Science; from Duke, Wilburt C. Davison, dean of the School of Medicine, graduate dean Marcus Hobbs, and W.J. Seeley, dean of engineering; from N.C. State, in addition to Lampe, Malcolm Campbell of textiles and Dean Colvard from the School of Agriculture.

The Working Committee's greatest value was in demonstrating to the business-oriented Development Council that the universities were actively engaged. While their role was education and basic research, not research for industry, they offered cooperation, professional guidance and consultation and, above all, the environment of scientific, medical, and cultural inquiry that was so crucial in the task of bringing concept to actuality.

Both university presidents were favorable to the concept and agreeable to participating. "At the same time," Simpson has written, "knowing the hazards and knowledgeable of their own responsibilities, they were plain spoken to the effect that they would not acquiesce in anything that was detrimental to the character and the basic educational and research programs of their institutions."

Mindful of this reservation, the Working Committee fashioned a statement of purpose: "The basic concept of the Research Triangle is that North Carolina possesses a unique combination of educational and research resources and communications facilities eminently suitable to the fostering of industrial research. It is not anticipated that the three universities shall engage directly in the conduct of industrial research, except under carefully designed and administered policies. Rather, the principal functions of the universities are to stimulate industrial research by the research atmosphere their very existence creates and to supplement industrial research talents and facilities by providing a wellspring of knowledge and talents for the stimulation and guidance of research by industrial firms."

Another Working Committee achievement came from a Subcommittee for Inventory, chaired by Marcus Hobbs and including Colvard, Davison, and R.J.M Hobbs. On November 15, 1955, they completed a densely packed, 200-page *Inventory of Selected Resources of the Research Triangle*. It was a comprehensive listing of resources in science, medicine, the humanities and performing arts, libraries, and special equipment, and included data on city and county government, transportation, public education, and cultural and historical attractions right down to "the quaint little house [in Raleigh] in which the seventeenth President of the United States, Andrew Johnson, was born."

With a result that's reported three paragraphs below, the Working Committee also pressed for the hiring of an executive.

Responding to the Development Council's need for money, especially if an executive was to be hired and promotional activity expanded, Hanes suggested in July 1956 that a nonprofit organization was needed to secure tax benefits for contributors. "Characteristically," Herbert wrote for a talk on March 11, 1975, "the Governor answered 'You and Brandon work out something.' He hated to be bothered with details, and work out something they did."

The nonprofit Research Triangle Committee* was incorporated on September 25, 1956, replacing the Development Council and with almost the same membership: Hanes as chairman, Armstrong, Edens, Floyd, Brandon Hodges, Gov. Hodges, Rankin, Reynolds, and Ruffin. The one change was the addition of Friday, who had succeeded Gordon Gray as UNC's president.

The governor had already asked Friday to provide the committee with an executive director from the university and on the same day, September 25, 1956, Simpson's appointment to this post was announced. The choice could hardly have been happier. For imaginative grasp of the concept, careful planning, judiciousness, ability to get along with academics and businessmen alike, and immeasurable tact, Simpson was just about perfect. Commenting on just one facet of Simpson's performance, Duke history professor Hamilton wrote that "In a period when successes were few, problems many, tempers therefore short, and natural rivalries extant, he kept the leaders, each a mogul in his own principality, working as a team . . . ."

In addition to Simpson's personal and professional qualities, Friday's selection also took into account earlier associations with the late Howard W. Odum, a highly regarded UNC sociology professor and innovative scholar. He had founded, in 1924, UNC's Institute for Research in Social Science and was noted for his interest in regional development and economic issues. Chapel Hill partisans sometimes credit Odum with creating the research triangle concept. He didn't, but he did contribute to the frame of mind—Gray's, Friday's, Simpson's, for example—which led to its acceptance. Hodges correctly recorded that Odum "talked of a research institute for the development of southern resources to be operated jointly by the University and State College," and one of Odum's proposals would have located a cooperative activity at the airport, convenient to both State and Carolina. Duke wasn't

* This was the committee's chartered name. An unofficial variation that Simpson created to embellish letterhead and some publications was "Governor's Research Triangle Committee."

included, however, nor were the physical and engineering sciences. Odum's plans didn't envision nonacademic applications research as a vehicle for industrial growth; his contributions to his university and profession lay in other directions. As his teacher and later as his fellow faculty member, Odum influenced Simpson and won his admiration. In a 1966 letter to UNC's Louis R. Wilson, Simpson described his older colleague's relation to the Research Triangle. Far too modestly on his own behalf, but accurately, he wrote, "To the extent that I was important to the enterprise, then Dr. Odum was directly and palpably involved."

Simpson started to work on October 1, 1956. Joining him in a former residence on Edenton Street in downtown Raleigh was Elizabeth J. Aycock, office manager and secretary. Until her retirement to part-time status at the end of 1989, Aycock served not only in those capacities, but also as RTFoundation assistant treasurer, bookkeeper, corporate secretary, and non-pareil meeter, greeter, and expositor. Pearson Stewart was hired in January 1958 as associate director for planning. As RTFoundation vice president, he, too, retired to a part-time role at the end of 1989.

Aycock remembers that Simpson began firing off "wonderful," comprehensive letters to industrial prospects and flying off to present his case in person. She's still impressed at how rapidly and skillfully the academic sociologist became a demon industrial development promoter.

Salaries, supplies, travel, consultants' fees, and promotional materials were paid for by contributions from the local communities, those that would benefit most from any Research Triangle development. Without their prior commitment, statewide support was unlikely. Fund raising responsibilities fell chiefly to Watts Hill in Durham, banker George P. Geohegan, Jr., and printing executive G. Akers Moore, Jr., in Raleigh, and Collier Cobb, Jr., chairman of the Bank of Chapel Hill.

Hill's files show cash receipts of $41,278 for the year beginning October 1, 1956, and $32,599 for 1957-58. The two-year totals indicate $12,500 from Winston-Salem, $5,725 from Greensboro, and $2,000 from Charlotte, with the balance from the Triangle communities. Most contributions were under $500. Nineteen companies gave $1,000 or more.

Simpson's early activities included expanding his acquaintanceships at State and Duke, getting to know his RTCommittee business colleagues and state government officials, and helping his traveling band of faculty ambassadors prepare printed materials on the Triangle's resources and current research in their areas of specialty. The brochure on "Resources for Research in Chemistry" listed UNC's William Little as RTCommittee associate director for chemistry, and that on "Resources for Research in Electronics" listed State's William Stevenson as assistant director for electronics. Other discipline-oriented pamphlets covered industrial engineering and forestry. Like the committee's more general publications produced by Simpson, they described the universities, the region and the three cities, the research atmosphere, ongoing research, special equipment available, cultural and community assets.

In a document dated October 1958, Simpson reported that "it is realistic to think that national companies and agencies of the federal government will establish laboratories in the Research Triangle." Citing the scores of visits made by faculty members, Stewart, and himself, he added that "More than 25 visits have been made to the Research Triangle by industrial people.* The general verdict is that the Research Triangle qualifies well." He also noted that "The Research Triangle Committee concluded that the establishment of a research institute in a research park in the center of the Research Triangle would be the most effective single thing that could be done in the development of the Research Triangle . . . ."

Yet as late as June 1958, three months earlier, none of the RTCommittee's descriptive literature mentioned a Research Triangle Park. Real estate was central to Simpson's and the committee's dealings, but promotional mentions of the RTPark were left primarily to Guest and the Pinelands Company, Inc.

Pinelands provides a tangled tale that's best attempted without lawyerly idiom. George Herbert presented it unadorned during a March 1975 speech from which the following excerpt is taken:

"These faculty salesmen were handicapped, however, by the lack of anything to sell. Only a general area with a university environment. The first proposal from N.C. State in January 1955, had recommended a park, and this recommendation had been repeated several times in communications to the Governor. In February, 1957, Simpson—obviously troubled by the lack of something to sell—asked if the three communities (Raleigh, Durham, and Chapel Hill) could not combine in the purchase of the necessary land.

"Under pressure to assemble a site for the 'great research centers,' and failing to find local money, Hodges was reminded of a friend and acquaintance, Karl Robbins, by Bill Saunders, director of the Department of Conservation and Development who had worked with Robbins. As Hodges would write later, 'We began looking for an angel.' Robbins, who had sold his extensive textile holdings in the state, seemed a good prospect, and the

* Including N.M. Martin of New York, the IBM Corporation's vice president for facilities planning and construction. His visit in February 1958 was the company's introduction to the Research Triangle. Although IBM had "no current requirement for a facility suitable to this . . . locality," Martin told Guest that he was "genuinely interested in receiving periodic information . . . ." Ten years later, Watts Hill commented that "old Romeo was right on the ball in '58."

Governor suggested that Saunders try to arrange a meeting. Robbins finally was reached by telephone at the Sun and Surf Club in Palm Beach and accepted an invitation to breakfast at the Mansion. The meeting was held on April 12, 1957, and, in addition to the Governor, the only others present for the breakfast discussions with Robbins were Saunders and George Simpson. Hodges began to describe Triangle opportunities and problems, proposing it would be both sound [business] and a public service for Robbins to buy and develop the necessary land. He had talked for no more than five minutes when their guest interrupted with a most encouraging response.

"As Hodges would remember it later, Robbins said, 'You need not say anything more, Luther. I understand. It is a wonderful idea and a money-maker. I'll back you and will put up to a million dollars in the project.'

"A phrase which has become overworked in recent years might have been appropriate as Saunders and Simpson left the Mansion that April morning: 'We see light at the end of the tunnel.'

"In the optimistic weeks that followed, the light seemed to grow even brighter. In May, Robbins informed the Governor that Guest had been authorized to secure options on up to 5,000 acres of land and to prepare a budget for a two-million-gallon per day water line from Durham, and on September 10 Hodges called a press conference to announce that Robbins already had spent $750,000 for land and would spend $250,000 more for utilities. Shortly thereafter Robbins formed the Pinelands Company to hold and develop the land, with himself as Chairman and Guest as President.

"Throughout the 1957 period of difficulties and decisions, Governor Hodges' enthusiasm never waned. He continued to extol the virtues of the Research Triangle, and its expected impact on per capita income, to such diverse audiences as a joint meeting of civic clubs in Greensboro; a luncheon in Pinehurst for representatives of North Carolina Independent Telephone Companies; [an] industry hunting luncheon in New York, sponsored by the three electric utilities operating in North Carolina; and a meeting of the Men's Fellowship Group of Pritchard Memorial Baptist Church in Charlotte.

"The year 1957 saw another development of special importance to me, the first planning for a contract research institute as an integral part of the total Research Triangle program. Dr. Gross had proposed this at Hodges' first luncheon meeting with university representatives in February, 1955, and Simpson had included an institute in his first set of planning recommendations to the Research Triangle Committee in January, 1957. The recommendation was accepted; a subcommittee established, headed by Brandon Hodges, and the institute planning group held its first meeting in Gross's office at Duke on March 5, 1957.

"The fall of 1957 turned out to be a grim and disheartening time for Triangle leaders. The nation was feeling the effects of recession, and three firms that had visited the area during the summer backed away. Brandon Hodges, the former State Treasurer and Champion Paper executive who had carried more of the earlier burden than is remembered today, died that fall. Robert Hanes succumbed to an illness that would take his life within 18 months, and Karl Robbins began to grow cool toward the plan.

"Robbins had not, in fact, invested quite as much as Governor Hodges had been led to believe before his September 10 press conference, there were substantial land options to be picked up in 1958, and there were substantial unsecured gaps remaining in the area we know today as the Research Triangle Park.

"Robbins' ardor had been dampened partially by the slow pace of negotiations with the City of Durham and partially by advice he was receiving in New York. Whatever the reasons, he announced he would put in no more money until North Carolinians matched his investment dollar for dollar. Despite desperate overtures, including a trip to Palm Beach by Romeo Guest, wining and dining in the Triangle area, and meetings with the Governor, the university presidents, and the mayor of Durham, Robbins never did resume his support.

"Perhaps more important, however, he did agree in October, 1958, to turn over to the nonprofit Research Triangle Committee or Research Triangle Foundation, as it was soon to become known, his investment in the Pinelands real estate venture at original cost, or without profit, giving the Foundation ownership of the Research Triangle Park.

"1958 was to be one of several turning point years. Governor Hodges appointed George Watts Hill, of Durham, to replace Brandon Hodges on both the Research Triangle Committee and the Research Institute Committee, and Hill immediately demonstrated that he would be one of the most potent contributors to ultimate success. At a speech in Durham in January, 1959, Hodges would acknowledge 'a great debt of gratitude . . . owed . . . Watts Hill, Sr., for the work he had done. Without the magnificent leadership and untiring service of men such as this, the Research Triangle might still be nothing more than another good idea, or a gleam in someone's eye.'

"In other leadership roles, George Simpson extended his university leave for another year, and an associate of the ailing Hanes, Wachovia chairman Archie K. Davis, agreed to see if he could stir up any North Carolina investments.

"Hodges remained confident or, at least, determined. He simply refused to be associated with anything less than total success. In a one-month period in the spring of 1958, he boosted the Triangle in speeches in New York,

Birmingham, Alabama, Chapel Hill, and Clayton, referring, on one occasion, to 'our dynamic Research Triangle' as 'one of the leading research facilities in the nation.' There were squirrels in the pines and foxes deep in the woods in 1958, but unfortunately they had little human company.

"Archie Davis' search for investors was largely unsuccessful, but in early August, 1958, he and the Governor flew to meet with Hanes at Atlantic Beach, carrying with them the idea that would save the Triangle. Davis proposed a new concept: buy out Robbins and turn the entire project into a nonprofit program for the benefit of the state, its people, and the universities. Rather than seeking investors, solicit contributions. Hanes was skeptical and Hodges hopeful, but both agreed on the condition that Davis lead the fund raising drive.

"In October, Robbins agreed to transfer his ownership and Davis had established a goal of $1,250,000 — $500,000 to start the planned institute, $250,000 for a building, $250,000 for a water main, and the balance for operating what would be the Research Triangle Foundation.

"That is about the end of Chapter One. At the end of December, the Research Triangle Committee became the Research Triangle Foundation, and the Research Triangle Institute was incorporated.

"On January 9, 1959, several hundred people, representing leadership from across the state, gathered for a luncheon at the Sir Walter Hotel in Raleigh. With extensive radio and TV coverage, Governor Hodges announced that private and corporate citizens of the state had contributed and pledged $1,425,000. Appropriate credit was given to Archie K. Davis, and Robert M. Hanes was present, his last public function before his death in March.

"The Research Triangle program had been funded and was on its way."

Herbert's account includes several omissions, if such a feat is possible, some of which call for elaboration.

While the January 1955 "after midnight" proposal by Campbell and Newell did not use the word "park," it did specify "the development of an area between Raleigh, Durham and Chapel Hill and near the Raleigh-Durham Airport, as a center for industrial research," and Newell sketched a possible location for it very near the eventual boundaries. The center idea drew acceptance right away, something tangible, salable, at last. The term "research park" entered the triangle planners' vocabulary, and two years later Karl Robbins was brought into the picture to underwrite its development.

When Robbins authorized him, in the spring of 1957, to begin assembling the land, Guest was ready. To identify contiguous parcels and secure options, he engaged William Maughan, a consulting forester and one-time manager of Duke Forest, urging a low profile to muffle publicity and keep prices reasonable, meaning around $100 per acre. By mid-July nearly 1,700 acres were under option, the figure rising to about 3,500 acres in early September.

The sparsely populated land wasn't worth much. Herbert referred to the pines. Other common descriptors of how it looked were rolling hills, second-growth scrub, marginal family farms, empty fields, modest and scattered residences, broomsedge, and an unknown number of stills. He also mentioned squirrels and foxes. Among the area's other animal kingdom representatives, the alliterative "possums and Ph.D.s" were to find favor with editors in later years. And one former resident told the *Durham Morning Herald* that he sold his 32 acres for $20,000, adding, "You know, the biggest objection I had to the Research Triangle Park was that they took all the turkeys. That was great turkey land. I hunted every day I was off and I reckoned I killed 116 turkeys during the years we lived there."

Under his agreement with Guest, Robbins right away made $15,000 available for land options as part of a promised $500,000 for all land costs and $250,000 for a water line from Durham, a total commitment of $750,000. Several months later, on September 25, 1957, the Pinelands Company was incorporated. Financial aspects of Pinelands/RTPark will be touched upon briefly, and broadly, in later paragraphs.

Returning to Herbert's talk, a contract research institute was indeed "an integral part of the total Research Triangle program." In the end (in the beginning, rather) its official status differed from the original plans in two significant respects.

The first is, 31 years later, hard to believe. Even though all Research Triangle participants had come to regard an institute and its building as "the keys to the success of the Pinelands Park," the two organizations did not necessarily hold common ground. Not until a Watts Hill memo of September 8, 1958, was it explicitly stated that RTI was "to be located in the Park on a campus of at least 200 acres as the focal point . . . ." Up until then the committees, their chairmen, and Simpson were agreed that "RTI is not dependent upon the Park, since [it] can be located anywhere in the Triangle area which is reasonably convenient to the three university units."

This memo of Hill's also contained the acknowledgment that RTI would be owned by the Foundation as its research arm, as Pinelands would be its park-developing arm. It was the last time such a statement was made.

On that same September 1958 evening at the Mansion, Gov. Hodges convened a meeting of the utmost import for the Research Triangle institutions. In Research Triangle terms, if any meeting deserves momentous as a modifier, this is it. Attending were Archie Davis, William Friday, Paul Gross, Romeo Guest, Watts Hill, William P. Saunders (more about him in a minute), George Simpson, Pearson Stewart, and William Whyburn.

Topic A was money, making sure of general agreement on Research Triangle goals, principles, and policies before Davis undertook his fund-raising mission. There was little question that general agreement did exist, but this was the moment of decision and Davis needed the others' endorsements.

During the discussion both Friday and Gross voiced strong reservations about RTI's role as a subsidiary ultimately responsible to the Foundation. Hill's notes of the meeting reflect nothing adversarial (his notes are, needless to say, masterly), for everyone agreed with Friday that without RTI there was nothing. Friday went on to urge "an academic home" for RTI in order to foster its relationships with the university faculties. Davis concurred, up to a point, saying that RTI could run itself, but that the RTI board would report to the Foundation as the overall governing body that would supply the first funding and might be asked for more.

Here Gross concurred, up to a point, seeing no reason for any real conflict. However, he argued that university people must control RTI, and that there would be "strenuous objection" if control should rest with an independent corporate body such as the Foundation. Gross said, and the quotation is again from Hill's notes, "It's not separation but cooperation. The going will be rough in the beginning and that's when an *enlightened* board is needed more than at any other time." (Emphasis added.) He went on to say that RTI must of course put in the best manager, "but the Foundation will not be allowed to select him." Friday weighed in with the confirming observation that the universities would approve if RTI was "protected organizationally," an evident euphemism for university governance.

By meeting's end the issues it was called to consider were resolved and understood. Davis went forth to organize for a campaign to raise more than one million dollars. Simpson and Hill were free to begin devising articles and by-laws that would vest control of RTI in the universities.

(In response to Davis's comment about possible financial assistance to RTI beyond the start-up $500,000, Gross, according to Hill's notes, preferred to think of RTI developing under its own steam rather than being dependent on the Foundation. He had confidence that RTI could stand on its own feet, but felt there was a question about Pinelands' ability to do so. He worried that, if Pinelands got into trouble, the two organizations should not be tied so closely that Pinelands' failure would pull RTI down. At this point, Hill's notes record, "Guest commented that Pinelands' profits will not show up for at least five years, the sales will go very slowly, promotional costs will be heavy, cost at least $40,000 for a good man and his operating expenses, Pinelands must pay income tax. By 15 years someone will reap a tremendous profit." Too bad Hill couldn't yet insert his own comment of 1968 that "old Romeo was right on the ball in '58.")

Davis acted immediately. Just three days after the September 8, 1958, discussions he met at the airport with Geohegan, Hill, and Simpson. He'd set a campaign goal of $1,250,000 minimum, asked Geohegan to raise at least $100,000 of it in Raleigh and Hill to do the same in Durham. A December 2 report shows they were successful. By the same date, Davis himself had "sold and signed" at least $400,000, including three one-hundred-thousand-dollar pledges. Except for the help he asked for in Raleigh and Durham, Elizabeth Aycock described Davis as preferring to go it alone.

He didn't do too badly. The minimum goal had already been surpassed when Hodges announced the $1,425,000 amount on January 9, 1959. The total later rose to more than two million. Not all of it was from corporate treasuries, either. Aycock deposited one check for $3.75 from a citizen who had faith.

Faith was the key all up and down the line, for campaign receipts weren't investments or loans, but donations by individuals and private companies that had faith in their governor, in their universities, and in men like the one who offered them the chance to participate. Davis promised each that if he fell short of the $1,250,000 goal, the pledges would no longer be binding.* Guest was right when he asserted that "By 15 years someone will reap a tremendous profit," although the Triangle region's prosperity has been a far more enriching consequence than any "someone's" gain. Hodges was also right a few years later when he called the Research Triangle Park, "the central fact in our state's economic future."

Skimming over Pinelands' and the Park's financial woes, Karl Robbins had been receptive and generous at a time when both qualities were badly needed, but he never came close to the "up to a million dollars" that Hodges expected and Guest counted on. He didn't even get half way to the $750,000 he promised Guest. As president of Pinelands, the latter knew scarcely a day free from worries about money. (He had other business activities to look after, too, many of them taken care of by his secretary, Phyllis Branch. Aycock enjoys telling about how they spoke to each other. The punctilious Guest addressed his secretary as Mrs. Branch. She called him Romeo.)

Amounts advanced by Robbins were sufficient to begin securing options and buying some land, to get started on negotiations for the water line, to pay for the inevitable legal fees, and for taxes, surveys, mapping, commissions,

* This was news to Herbert. Davis told him about the promise during half-time of a November football game in Chapel Hill, adding that he'd collected slightly more than half the goal. Herbert, who on October 1 had given notice to his New York employer and had committed his career and his family to North Carolina, gulped. One-third of a century later he says, with the barest hint of a small smile, that Davis still gets a kick out of telling the story.

title searches, travel, and other expenses. Sufficient, but far from enough to see the project through, even though Guest remained confident that the park's potential profitability would attract investors. He also remained confident that, even if other stockholders could not be found, Robbins would pay for all land and related costs.

As land acquisition and site planning progressed, Simpson kept Hanes and the RTCommittee informed. By the end of November 1957 Pinelands was incorporated and some 1,400 of the 3,500 optioned acres had been purchased for $220,125. Also, Robbins had changed his mind.

He would, he announced, guarantee a maximum expenditure of $260,000, not counting the first $15,000 in option money. Since $220,125 had already gone for land purchases, this represented an addition of only forty thousand. Anything more would have to come from sales of stock or bank loans.

Robbins' new ground rules surprised and disappointed Hodges, who said so, and were a blow to Guest, for costs steadily mounted. In a contract dated December 30, 1957, Robbins conveyed land and related assets to Pinelands for the $275,000 he had spent or committed, half of it in common stock, half in 20-year subordinated debentures.

Temporary relief had by then arrived through a $100,000 loan from William Saunders, a former associate of Robbins' in the textile business and one of his investment advisors. Saunders was at that time director of the N.C. Department of Conservation and Development, and a supporter of Research Triangle and Pinelands goals. The next summer he wanted to invest $50,000 in Pinelands stock. Gov. Hodges dissuaded him, however, feeling that such an ownership position wasn't appropriate for a public official.*

Three investors were obtained early in 1958 and a fourth joined them a few months later. They were Guest himself for $24,000, Ralph C. Price, retired president of Jefferson Standard Life Insurance Company in Greensboro, also for $24,000 and, at $10,000 each, A.A. Vanore and W.E. Alexander, both friends of Robbins from the Pinehurst area. That was all. Even Guest's brother wasn't interested.

Borrowing appeared to be the solution, if only a stopgap. In February a joint loan of $250,000 was agreed to by Wachovia, Durham Bank and Trust, and the Bank of Chapel Hill. This enabled Guest to run the company for several months and to purchase land on which options expired through March, April, and May. He ran short, however, and came out of the woods,

* Hodges took a hard line, properly so, on matters that involved conflicts of interest or, as in this case, the potential for perceptions of favoritism by government. Later on, he refused to let Pinelands publications contain even a hint of company associations with the Research Triangle Committee.

temporarily once again, only after Hill visited Robbins in New York during May. As a result of their meeting, Robbins made a $55,000 loan to Pinelands. Guest's July 31, 1958, financial statement could thus report purchases of 3,921 acres for $717,627. Including options that had to be picked up by January 3, 1959, Pinelands held title on that date to an additional 118 acres, a total of 4,039. Their average price was $508.

Simpson, meanwhile, had been growing uneasy about relationships between a not-for-profit institute and the private, for profit real estate development and now, faced with the dismal prospect of persistent lack of funds, perhaps even liquidation, the principals began to think about putting Pinelands on a public service, nonprofit basis. Davis's and Hodges' visit with Hanes in Atlantic Beach followed, and the Research Triangle emerged with a wholly new look.

Robbins was all for it. In October he told Hodges that he and the other Pinelands stockholders would transfer their ownership, at no profit to themselves, for unsecured notes. The way was cleared for Davis's fund-raising campaign, for the name change from Research Triangle Committee to Research Triangle Foundation, for the incorporation of RTI and, finally, for the public announcements of January 9, 1959.

But another financial trial lay ahead. Robbins died in January 1960. Settlement of his estate required that the notes be paid, so a crisis fell upon the new Research Triangle Foundation team. (Gordon Gray was chairman, Archie Davis president, and Akers Moore vice president. Moore was also president of Pinelands, "doing business as the Research Triangle Park" until the company's dissolution on September 30, 1965. Guest served on the Foundation board until May of 1959 and as a Pinelands director until the end of October the same year.)

Davis and Moore were undoubtedly familiar with Watts Hill's injunction that "North Carolina banks must realize that the old collateral of cotton and corn must be replaced with the more dynamic collateral of brains," but in this emergency they mortgaged their real estate to the tune of $1,300,000 borrowed from eight banks and eight insurance companies.

With these funds the Park/Pinelands paid Robbins' estate for his stock and loan, retired Saunders' loan, and repaid Guest and the three other stockholders. The proceeds also allowed them to purchase an additional 362 acres, including several "holes" that jeopardized the Park's physical integrity and completeness.

The Foundation's assets in land were substantial, but Friday was right in remembering that "there wasn't a spare nickel in the budget." The treasury was replenished for keeps when IBM bought 420 acres in the spring of 1965. Aycock recalls with pleasure the day the outstanding indebtedness was retired.

10. Gifts, Grants, and Surplus Earnings

Research Triangle Institute operates in most respects like any business. The major differences are that it doesn't have owners to whom it returns a profit or dividends, and that it is exempt from income taxes on earnings from most of its activities.

The Institute's purpose is public service, not profit. None of its net income may be used for the benefit of any individual or group of individuals. All net income is reinvested in, or held in reserve for, buildings and equipment, the development of staff and new research programs, and some supplemental support of fundamental and public service research.

RTI is also similar to other businesses in that income must exceed expenses. Otherwise it's out of business, for there is no endowment or subsidy.

Again like a private business, RTI requires capital. What is doesn't have is access to conventional markets for obtaining it. No stocks or bonds issued by RTI are available to investors.

The Institute's needs for capital are the usual ones: the equivalent of risk capital to finance start-up; capital to invest in buildings and equipment; and working capital to fund operations.

Gifts and grants have helped significantly, no question about it, but by far the greatest proportion of RTI capital has come from net income, earned surpluses generated by the work of its staff and consisting primarily of contract fees.

Accumulated net invested in research facilities and operations was $24 million at the end of the 1989 fiscal year, a 30-year total that reflects an operating surplus every year since cash break-even was achieved in the spring of 1961. It also reflects a cost-conscious central administration, and project leaders whose management skills match their technical proficiencies.

Capital to supplement RTI's own cash generation has come from both public and private sources. First place among them is held by the Research Triangle Foundation, whose $500,000 from the contributions raised by Archie Davis was RTI's start-up funding.

It cannot be repeated too often that those contributions of $2,000,000 to the RTFoundation from individual and corporate citizens of North Carolina were a remarkable show of faith in the diverse group of academic and business leaders who earnestly believed their Research Triangle dream could become a reality and whose determination made it so.

RTI's half-million-dollar share of the private donations was disbursed in periodic increments from February 1959 through February 1962. Payments initially were acknowledged by promissory notes bearing interest of five percent, which was carried on RTI's books, but not paid. As planned, accrued interest was subsequently forgiven and the notes converted to donations.

The private sector fund-raising campaign's success convinced Governor Hodges that other North Carolinians shared his enthusiasm and that some material evidence of public support was in order.

So, following up on an informal recommendation that had first been made by Simpson and the Research Institute Committee the previous September, the governor included a line item of $200,000 specified for RTI equipment in the biennial budget he submitted to the General Assembly's 1959 spring session. Herbert accompanied Hill to testify about it at an Appropriations Committee hearing and was impressed, to say the least, that his chairman of the board met not only with success but also with a standing ovation from the committee members.

The legislature's grant-in-aid was a giant boost, combining with the Atomic Energy Commission contract to assure the proper equipping and outfitting of initial laboratory activities. One-half of the appropriation was deposited in a special bank account in the summer of 1959 and one-half the following year.

In 1963 Governor Terry Sanford went his predecessor one better, more precisely one hundred thousand better. At his behest, and following months of preparation by himself and the technical group headed by Paul Gross and Buck Menius, the General Assembly created the N.C. Board of Science and Technology. North Carolina thus became the first state in the nation to appropriate substantial funding intended specifically to stimulate scientific, engineering, and industrial R&D through grants to the state's colleges, universities, research institutes, and high-tech industry laboratories.

Representing RTI, Herbert was closely involved in plans for the new state agency and also gave Sanford regular progress reports on Institute affairs. During one meeting the governor asked him (and Herbert isn't likely to forget the question), "What could you do with three hundred thousand dollars?" "Double the size of the Institute," was the reply. So the appropriations bill funding the new agency included a line item that earmarked $300,000 for RTI equipment and instrumentation, purchases that would greatly enhance the Institute's ability to compete successfully for research contracts in the laboratory sciences.

Four years later, with Governor Dan K. Moore sitting as chairman, the N.C. Board of Science and Technology responded to RTI requests with an award of $200,000 to acquire a list of specific equipment items for research in drug metabolism, agricultural chemicals, and air and water pollution.

This third State of North Carolina general grant raised state participation in equipping RTI to $700,000. But it wasn't a one-way street. Over the same period of time, nearly nine years, RTI operations had generated $20 million in research revenue, virtually all of it from sources outside North Carolina, which was cycled into the state's economy in the form of salaries and wages, buildings, and expenditures for materials, supplies, and services. And by this time the Research Triangle Park, with RTI at its heart, was well on the way to becoming one of the scientific world's wonders.

In December 1969, Governor Robert W. Scott announced a Board of Science and Technology equipment award of $160,000 to RTI. This amount increased the State of North Carolina's investment in RTI to $860,000. It was still a good one, for by then the Institute's cumulative revenues had reached $33 million.

All except the first two grants originated by Hodges and Sanford were won on a competitive basis. With competition for available dollars growing keener as the state's technology base broadened, RTI's requests and awards grew more modest, averaging about twenty thousand dollars annually for the next seven or eight years, then ceased at a total of almost exactly one million. Major acquisitions in several fields of research included a combined gas chromatograph-mass spectrometer for identifying drug and pesticide residues, a motorized environmental laboratory for on-site air sampling at locations in several states ranging as far as California, a pulsed Fourier transform NMR facility for biomedical studies, and a photographic recorder and scanning radiometer for RTI's satellite receiving station.

At the time of Gov. Scott's December 1969 announcement, RTI had invested $7.5 million in physical facilities. This amount included the state's grants, as well as gifts and some mortgage financing. The much larger balance, however, was from those net earnings on research revenue that were generated by the technical staff's ability to win contracts and to manage them successfully.

Corporate and personal donors, in addition to those who rallied to Archie Davis's banner in 1958-59, have contributed appreciably to RTI's resources.

The biggest award was the Dreyfus Foundation's $2,500,000, but by the time the Camille Dreyfus Laboratory began operations in the fall of 1961 it had more than the original grant going for it. By then the Celanese Corporation had approved an agreement under which RTI received a total of $1 million over five years for unrestricted basic research in polymer science.

December 1961 was the date of Grover M. Hermann's first public association with RTI. Thanks in very large part to Gov. Sanford's initiative, Hermann, who was chairman of the Martin Marietta Corporation and became a 15-year member of RTI's board, pledged $100,000 toward a 20,000-square-foot laboratory and office building. He stipulated that it was to be named in honor of the late William Trent Ragland, former president of the Superior Stone Company, a North Carolina subsidiary of Martin Marietta. Possibly by coincidence, the latter company contributed an additional $51,000 toward the building's construction.

In the spring of 1964 Hermann provided another gift, this one of $60,000 toward the purchase of a BR-340, a digital computer made by the Bunker-Ramo Corporation, then a subsidiary of Martin Marietta. Possibly by coincidence, the company extended an educational discount to RTI for the purchase.

Hermann's generosity hardly ended there. When Herbert was on one of his swings to bring non-Triangle board members up to date on Institute affairs, he met with Hermann in Chicago. Over lunch, he expressed frustration at the difficulties he faced in financing the long-wanted, greatly needed new laboratory building for chemistry and life sciences. Hermann asked if $335,000 would help. It would indeed, but in the excitement of answering Herbert forgot to say thank-you for the lunch.

At the annual Board of Governors meeting on November 1, 1967, Herbert announced the Grover Hermann Foundation's $335,000 pledge that would at last allow chemistry and life sciences to move from bursting-at-the-seams Bacon Street to shiny new quarters on campus. The board helped him say thank-you by deciding to name the building for Grover M. Hermann.

Watts Hill joined the Hermann Building act in 1969. Seven years earlier he had purchased a 49-acre tract adjacent to the Park, stating his intention to protect it as a future laboratory site for disposal by the Research Triangle Foundation. In 1968 he transferred title to the Durham Foundation with the stipulation that proceeds from an eventual sale were to be shared by RTI, as principal beneficiary, and by Durham Academy, an independent school Hill and his wife founded in 1933. The sale occurred in the summer of 1969. A Baltimore construction firm bought the property on which to build facilities for lease to what was then the National Air Pollution Control Administration which became, in 1970, the U.S. Environmental Protection Agency.

RTI realized $200,000 for its new building from the transaction, Durham Academy got $77,000, and the Research Triangle Park got the EPA.

It would be several years before Hill did anything else for RTI except carry out his duties as chairman of the board; faithfully attend executive committee meetings; help keep fences mended with the universities, state government, and the RTFoundation; guide Herbert in setting Institute policies; advise him on financial and operating problems; and tirelessly promote RTI's interests at every opportunity.

Then in 1973 Hill made a substantial pledge toward a planned research office building to relieve the Ragland Building space jam on social and statistical sciences. At that year's November annual meeting, Herbert announced an increase in Hill's pledge that would provide for addition of a corporate headquarters floor, bringing Hill's total gift toward the building to $250,000.

At the November 1974 annual meeting Herbert announced that this structure would be named for George Watts Hill. Saying that "Even if the building was sixty stories high instead of six, it would scarcely be adequate recognition of Mr. Hill's leadership," didn't satisfy Herbert as adequate recognition, but it was the best he could do at the time.

Nine years later he found a better solution, announcing at a dinner following the 25th annual meeting that the Board of Governors had approved an initial endowment of $100,000 to create the George Watts Hill Scholarship Fund for children of RTI staff members. The first annual disbursement for the National Merit Scholarships was made in 1985. Hill contributed personal funds to the endowment the same year, and several staff members have donated personal honoraria and speaking fees.

Money gifts in smaller amounts have also been given to RTI. In 1962 and 1964 grants of $2,000 each were made by the Herbert T. and Olive F. Randall Foundation of Ohio. Randall was R&D vice president at Champion International, in which capacity he had known Herbert and Ashton at Stanford, and he served on RTI's board for four years.

December 1963 was when the Central Carolina Bank made its first $500 donation. A similar sum has been paid annually ever since, except that from 1979 through 1981 CCB forgot and sent $600 instead. For the Durham Realty & Insurance Company, later Southland Associates, 1963 was also the first year for gifts ranging from $200 to $750 that were made annually through 1986.

In 1964 the Chemstrand Research Center donated $15,000 toward a cobalt-60 gamma-radiation source to expand RTI's resources for polymer studies. Through its own research on synthetic fiber products, Chemstrand's interests were akin to RTI's in studying how the molecular structure of polymeric materials can be modified by radioactive particle bombardment. Buried in a concrete structure across the road from the foot of the Dreyfus approach, the irradiation source is still serviceable, but has only occasional use as a research tool.

Structured fund-raising has never been tried by RTI. Board members and Herbert talked off and on during the sixties about methods for supplementing cash generation to finance capital needs, but anything like an organized campaign would inevitably be perceived to be in conflict with university development goals. The closest RTI came was in 1967 when, following Grover Hermann's lead, Liggett & Myers made a gift of $5,000 and the Burlington Industries Foundation pledged $30,000 over three years. Early in 1969 the BASF Corporation contributed $3,000.

Contributions in kind have, over the years, proved to be more readily available than those in cash, and often more valuable. They have come from a variety of sources dating back to the 1961 New Year's weekend when, without charge for labor or vans, the Raleigh Bonded Warehouse, Inc., moved both Institute and Foundation into the Hanes Building.

With the move accomplished, Charles E. Hayworth tore up the first of approximately $40,000 worth of office furnishings invoices. President of the Alma Desk Company in High Point, and an RTI board member for 14 years, Hayworth made the donations during RTI's early years and Alma Desk has continued to treat RTI in a kindly manner ever since.

In 1970, six years after RTI acquired its first Bunker-Ramo computer with Hermann's $60,000 and an educational discount, the TRW Corporation declared as surplus a much larger BR-340 that had an initial cost of a half-million dollars. Sam Ashton crafted a strategy by which RTI acquired it for $7,525.

One of the most cherished of all gifts was a $7,000 collection of statistical reference books, texts, journals, and other professional publications. It was given in January 1986 by Linda Drummond, widow of Douglas T. Drummond, an RTI senior statistician and department manager who died in a Washington, D.C., hospital the previous September after being hit by an automobile.

Earlier, in July 1981, the Hewlett-Packard Company contributed a gas chromatograph/mass spectrometer for identifying and measuring volatile chemicals like those found in samples of polluted air and water. The GC/MS was valued at $78,400.

April 1983 marked the first gift from the Gould, Inc., Computer Systems Division in Fort Lauderdale. It was a Concept 32/8750 super minicomputer worth $477,000 and used in very large scale integration (VLSI) work for commercial clients, the Department of Defense, and NASA. Other software and hardware gifts from Gould later the same year and, in February 1985, a replacement for the Concept's processor, greatly increased RTI's capabilities in computer-aided design, computer architecture research, and scientific word processing.

(Just five years later, the Gould super minicomputer had become obsolescent and was replaced by a network of seven desktop computers interconnected with RTI's network software product, Freedomnet™.)

To aid the Center for Aerosol Technology's state-of-the-art R&D on detecting, measuring, and controlling ultrafine particles that may contaminate semiconductor clean-room environments, Flanders Filters, Inc., of Washington, North Carolina, contributed a clean-room tunnel module in 1984.

Two companies made September 1987 donations to RTI's environmental measurements program. The Dexsil Corporation of Connecticut gave an analyzer for determining the levels of chlorine-containing compounds found in certain waste oils. From the Thermo-Jarrell Ash Corporation in Massachusetts, RTI received an atomic absorption spectrophotometer for analyzing trace-metal residues in fish and birds.

It must be recognized that gifts like those described in the last few paragraphs constitute effective product promotion for the donors. RTI recognizes this, and is glad to have the products.

This paragraph, however, may constitute the only advertising value that GE Microelectronics, a former RTI neighbor on Cornwallis Road, will derive from its donation of an estimated $50,000 worth of improvements, including air conditioners and raised flooring, for RTI's Ragland Computer Center, which was completely redesigned and renovated in 1988.

The most recent equipment grant that RTI has received, as of autumn 1989, was $12,500 from the North Carolina Biotechnology Center for instrumentation to be used in research on biological treatments of wastewater.

To RTI's own capital reserves, to State of North Carolina grants, and to personal, corporate, and foundation gifts, add the federal government as a major source for equipment acquisition. Through contracts calling for R&D that requires access to certain systems, instruments, and related supplies, hundreds upon hundreds of thousands of dollars worth of materiel has been made available to RTI by the National Institutes of Health, the EPA, DoD, and NASA. After certain use and maintenance standards are met, a client agency often considers the equipment to be obsolete and vests outright title in the Institute. In other situations, the agency retains title while RTI retains the apparatus. In many cases similar facility benefits are also derived from relationships with private sector clients.

RTI units in all the laboratory sciences have benefited. So have their clients, for the device, system, or facility not only accomplishes its original purpose, it also remains on-line for similar or separate follow-on contract work.

The kinds of instrumentation acquired with federal clients' funds are so numerous and so varied that none is representative. It would be bootless to try to identify most, or even some.

One example, however, though scarcely typical, illuminates the spirit of cooperation and the sharing of resources and benefits so often mentioned in the context of the Research Triangle enterprise.

The object in question is a model 902 high resolution, double focusing mass spectrometer. Its delivery to RTI's Bacon Street laboratory on September 1, 1967, signaled the start of a Regional Mass Spectrometry Center tailored uniquely by and for the Research Triangle.

Aptly described then as "the Supreme Court of small amounts," despite its 7,000 pounds, the instrument could measure the mass of chemical trace amounts with what was, at that time, unprecedented accuracy.

The NIH grant of $175,000 for the mass spec itself and related instrumentation came nearly three years after Monroe Wall expressed the desire for such a facility to support RTI research on novel steroids, hormone synthesis, tumor inhibitors, and drug metabolism. RTI alone clearly couldn't justify a request for such a sum, however, nor, although they too were interested, could any of the chemistry departments at UNC, Duke, or State.

So they resorted to a Research Triangle solution. All four institutions submitted the grant application jointly, and the resulting NIH award created one of only half a dozen such installations in the United States, and the only one in the south.

Regional in all respects, the center was located at and operated by RTI in conjunction with the universities. In addition to helping meet the analytical needs of their scientific, public health, and medical researchers, it also served the National Institute of Environmental Health Sciences and the National Center for Air Pollution Control (later the EPA's Environmental Research Center), both of them Research Triangle Park occupants, and the Bowman Gray School of Medicine in Winston-Salem.

Not quite a dinosaur at age 22, and no longer a multi-institutional operation, the facility still produces spectra that are useful for RTI research.

11. Acquiring the Campus and Buildings

I. Amazing Ambiguities

In a memo of December 3, 1959, to RTPark president Akers Moore, RTI chairman Watts Hill recorded Moore's comment that "probably [the] RTI campus should eventually be owned, operated, and maintained by RTI, final decision to be made upon advice of legal counsel and tax advisers." The statement reflected the generally agreed upon, but uncommitted, sentiment of RTFoundation, RTPark, and RTI officers. But what was it that RTI was to own?

157.81 acres is correct.

180 acres is convenient, and was used for many years.

The "amazing ambiguities," George Herbert's phrase, refer partly to the method of the land's disposition and partly to years of varying estimates that ranged from 288 acres to 250 acres to 200 acres.

As for when RTI was to own them, a final resolution wasn't reached until January 1972, a whole 12 years later. Even then, the Foundation's announcement referred to "the Institute's campus of 200 acres." RTI's "Masterplan," prepared later the same year by Six Associates, described an RTI site of "approximately 158 acres."

The convenience of 180 acres arises partly from visual reasons. There is no barrier between RTI's campus property and the site of the Foundation's Robert M. Hanes Memorial Building. Good thing, too, for if a fence or brick wall were to be erected on the softball field behind Hanes, rightfielders would be separated from second basepersons.

Reasons of spirit matter at least as much as, and surely more than, line-of-sight considerations. Monies for constructing the Hanes Building were specifically identified as memorial gifts to the Foundation in the name of Robert Hanes; the Foundation's Hanes Building is the Research Triangle Park's hub and headquarters; Foundation funds launched RTI; from 1961 through 1965 the Hanes Building housed segments of RTI research operations; beginning January 2, 1961, and on into the foreseeable future it is home for various RTI administrative offices.

Foundation and Institute share a heritage of name, goals, and achievement. Geographically the two institutions should be and are seamless.

During the formative years and through the early sixties, the boundaries that would enclose the Foundation's acreage gift to RTI were commonly understood to be: toward the north, Cornwallis Road; toward the south, what is now Interstate 40; toward the west, what is now the Durham Freeway; toward the east, Davis Drive and encompassing those parcels now occupied by the N.C. Science and Technology Research Center, the Chemical Industry Institute of Toxicology, the National Center for Health Statistics, and the Park recreation center (ready for action in 1990) in the hollow between RTI and STRC. The Foundation, Park, and RTI agreed that these limits defined a tract of 288 acres.

However, a June 1959 preliminary site plan and a September 1960 Long Range Plan for the campus both stated that the site contained approximately 250 acres. Nobody took exception.

According to an October 21, 1966, letter from Moore to RTF chairman Luther Hodges*, "... the Institute's campus has always been considered to be 199.09 acres by actual survey. Although ... Archie [Davis] agreed that it was 288 acres, I am sure that he had forgotten the details . . . and that after . . . renew[ing] his memory he would agree that the campus was approximately 200 acres."

These ambiguities were not as important to RTI as the piecemeal deeding of campus parcels, and a sense that the Foundation sought to regain a measure of control over the university-owned Institute's management of its own destiny.

In November of 1960 Hill, chairman of RTI's board and secretary of the Foundation's, reported to the RTI governors that "The policy of the Foundation will be to make parcels of the campus land available to the Institute as needed." At the time, this "as needed" qualification seemed unexceptionable.

The first land transfer from Foundation to Institute had already occurred, the 16.29 acres donated in October 1960 for the Camille Dreyfus Laboratory. In the same month RTI's Executive Committee voted the Foundation an appropriate resolution of "appreciation and gratitude."

A second donation of 8.03 acres was made late in 1962 for building #3. (Although never referred to as such, Hanes was #1, Dreyfus #2.) On December 12 another resolution of appreciation and gratitude was voted.

* Hodges became Foundation chairman early in 1965 after returning home from four years in Washington as U.S. Secretary of Commerce.

A major event of 1962 was the December announcement of Grover Hermann's pledge of $100,000 toward a fourth structure that was to become the William Trent Ragland Building.* In October 1963 RTI's Executive Committee authorized Herbert to begin negotiations with the Foundation for a Ragland Building site. By February 1964 mortgages had been arranged, construction cost estimates brought within budget, and the Foundation's gift of 18.33 acres acknowledged by the customary resolution of appreciation and gratitude.

Thirty years later there may be more than incidental interest in the fact that the early 288-acre quandary related to some wished-for but unrealized campus features. Proposals strongly backed by Hill, and sketched in the 1960 Long Range Plan, envisioned that the eastern 88-acre portion would contain a lake of about 40 acres, several guest houses, and a convention and exhibition hall including what Hill hoped would become a museum for displaying products of companies which had laboratories in the Park and other products from manufacturers in the Triangle area and throughout the state. Nothing came of the proposals, although Pinelands deeded the 88 acres to the Foundation, which reserved them for later disposition. The lake remained under consideration for another ten years before being termed physically impracticable. The recreation center now occupies part of that location.

In the end, the final configuration of RTI's campus was further diminished by 30.5 acres for interstate highway easements and rights of way, a southward realignment of Cornwallis Road, and intra-campus roads.

Moore's comment about RTI's eventual ownership of the campus was confirmed by the Foundation's Executive Committee. An excerpt from the minutes of its meeting on August 4, 1960, quotes Davis as observing that "there had never been a question as to the availability for Institute use of all the campus . . . ." But Moore's "eventually" seemed always a bit farther down the road. Through nearly the end of 1966 the Foundation had deeded just 42.65 acres for Dreyfus, #3, and Ragland.

During the preceding years of the Foundation's difficult financial period, RTI's officers hadn't the slightest intention of being anything but totally supportive. They deferred collection of what was owing for the Foundation's share of Hanes Building operating expenses and, for several years until the Pinelands Company's dissolution, they even paid the Foundation's Durham County property tax assessment on the 88 acres not included in the Hanes Building lease and being held for future sale or other disposition.

If treasuries could sigh, the Foundation's would have done so with immense relief following IBM's decision for the Research Triangle Park and

* For purposes of keeping count, Ragland was building 4. The 8.03 acres originally deeded for #3 also became the site for buildings 5, 6, and 7.

purchase of 420 acres. Soon thereafter, RTI board members determined to move ahead on the land ownership question that had been discussed for so long so often. They hadn't a hint that discussion would continue for six more years.

As an officer of both organizations' boards, Hill took the lead in arranging a Foundation to Institute invitation to discuss mutual relations. In addition to himself, three members from each executive committee met on September 29, 1966.

A week earlier he had gone through the formality of asking the RTI Executive Committee for suggestions of topics to be covered. To no one's surprise, the response was that "the principal policy item for discussion . . . be the transfer of the balance of the campus land," with Herbert commenting that "the addition to the balance sheet of this land intended for Institute use would have an important effect on demonstrating to government contracting agencies [our] financial strength." The committee unanimously voted a resolution requesting the Foundation "to donate the remaining portion of the Institute campus, less [the] Robert M. Hanes Building and its site, to the Research Triangle Institute in fee simple."

(Land was not only the principal policy item for discussion, but in reality the only one, for in other respects RTF/RTI relations were fine. Davis was, and still is, eloquent in praising RTI. Herbert was, and still is, tireless in his insistence on RTI's total dedication in support of the Foundation's mission to strengthen and build on the resources of the Park, and he loses no opportunity to explain RTI's role as just one element of the larger Research Triangle program. By turn, Ned E. Huffman, the Foundation's chief executive officer for 23 years beginning in 1965, and his successors have understood RTI's research mission and provided many valuable marketing contacts.)

At the September 29, 1966, meeting, Paul Gross, Marcus Hobbs, and Herbert presented RTI's resolution. Governor Hodges said it would be submitted to the Foundation board. Further, he asked for some documentation of the factors contributing to the request, including "indications of financial soundness." RTI's governors may have been surprised at this request for proof of a condition they thought was well established. They also were prepared. Within a week, under date of October 7, 1966, Hobbs in his capacity as RTI Executive Committee chairman composed a detailed statement entitled "On the Transfer of the 'Institute Campus' to the Research Triangle Institute."

The paper addressed sensitive issues with skill and delicacy. It reasoned forthrightly but without making demands, it spoke to attitudes which all knew existed but which no one overtly acknowledged, it identified stumbling blocks but wounded no feelings, it dealt with unfulfilled pledges but without rancor, it affirmed independence within the context of interdependence. It was, throughout, positive, tactful, logical. It also failed to achieve its immediate goal.

Over time, however, the transfer document succeeded; its influence proved strong and lasting. Before leaping ahead to the denouement of 1972, a review of several points made in Hobbs' 1966 statement provides insights to an understanding of RTI affairs. It is well to remember that at the time it was written RTI had grown to a staff of 282, had reached a $4.2 million annual revenue, had built four structures on campus and filled up the space at Bacon Street for a five-building capital investment of more than $2.5 million, and had received gifts of $2.8 million in addition to State of North Carolina equipment grants and the RTFoundation's original donation of start-up funds. All these "indications of financial soundness" were well known to the Foundation.

An early passage in the memorandum bowls a strike: "Important objectives and purposes of the... Institute beyond that of performing as a self-sustaining research organization, were to demonstrate that a thriving research activity could be achieved and supported in the Research Triangle Park, that such an activity was benefited by and was beneficial to the Triangle Universities, and by its example of success to assist in attracting additional research activity to the Triangle area and to the state. Thus, the primary challenge to the leadership of the Institute was to develop an unquestionably successful research institute operation and to do this as quickly as sound operation would allow... [A] successful operation has been achieved as of this date."

Further to this Triangle asset theme: "The existence of this successful operation, while not determinative in other Park successes, unquestionably has contributed in a significant way to the early achievement of some of these successes. It certainly contributed at an important time in the Park's development an exhibitable research activity of high quality; a tangible evidence, which otherwise might have been difficult to achieve, of cooperation among the several academic institutions and their direct and continuing interest in the total Park activity; and, in an almost unique manner, it has helped establish a national image of a successful Park—not just a successful Research Triangle Institute. The Institute has considered the above as part of its responsibility to the Park."

The university leaders who were engaged in Research Triangle affairs failed to share the concern expressed by Hodges, perhaps alone, that "the Institute will never make a direct contribution to the schools if it waits until its expansion is finished and its work is done." Such a dismaying misreading of RTI's nature and purpose—the very thought that RTI's life had a finite, limited term and, in particular, the completely mistaken implication that the

Institute's value to its founding universities was to be measured by dollar remittances—was remote from university perceptions.

As realists, officials and faculty members of the universities at no time harbored any expectation that RTI could, would, or should provide them with a direct financial contribution. They understood that the value of a successful Institute, and of other Park occupants as well, would be manifest in other coin: in scientific collegiality, in enriched educational resources, in employment opportunities for graduates, and in regional economic vitality.

The Hobbs paper anticipated Hodges' statement, which was made two years later and goes a long way toward explaining why the RTI Board of Governors' petition languished.

Hobbs touched on many aspects of the "thriving research activity . . . that . . . was benefited by and beneficial to the Triangle universities," and dealt straightforwardly with financial considerations.

After acknowledging the Foundation's start-up $500,000 grant for the third time in three pages, and why not?, Hobbs wrote that "The only other major asset planned by the Foundation for allocation to RTI has been the Institute Campus . . . . As of September 1966 the Foundation had, in fact, allowed the Institute to partially realize this asset by the transfer of 42.648 acres. It should be noted that, because of the corporate structure of the Institute, this was effectively a transfer to the Consolidated University of North Carolina and to Duke University and that . . . the same would be true of any further realization of the Institute Campus assets."

The Foundation's board had reservations about RTI's borrowing on these donated land parcels for the funds to erect and equip buildings. Hobbs felt no obligation to defend this customary and unavoidable practice, but did try to allay apprehensions about taking on risky debt. Thus: "In the future the Institute expects to handle requirements for equity capital and funds for equipment without jeopardy to such assets as campus sites; in construction of new facilities it will be the policy of the Institute to mortgage, and then only when necessary, not more than the facility and its site and not to mortgage land held for future building sites."

A matter Hobbs did feel obliged to defend was the management ability of the RTI board's Executive Committee. There was evidence, he wrote, that "The members of the Executive Committee present an array of talent in technical matters which characterize the major operational activities of the Institute, as well as evidence of capacity and extensive experience in dealing with financial affairs in major academic institutions and businesses."

Committee membership included six senior academic officials (four chemists, one physicist, one Renaissance literature specialist), one bank chairman, the former treasurer of an international utility, technical vice presidents from four Fortune 500 corporations, and one publishing company president, so it was probably unnecessary for Hobbs to underscore the sentence that read "It is felt that control of policy and financial matters by a committee of the constitution of the Executive Committee assures sound and reasonable decisions on matters which affect the financial ability of the Institute."

On November 2, 1966, Hobbs presented his paper to the Foundation. Writing to Hodges two weeks later, Hobbs stated he was "pleased that the Foundation feels the matter deserves further exploration," and also pleased that Hodges had "directed that the metes and bounds of the land enclosed by the four roads be determined as a step necessary before a decision can be made . . . ."

Exchanges about the transfer were renewed in the spring of 1968. In September RTI adopted its next-to-last resolution of appreciation and gratitude, this time for 5.99 acres as the site for what would become the Grover M. Hermann Laboratory Building for chemistry and life sciences.

Action on the larger issue was still not forthcoming, however, and Hill, Hobbs, and Herbert were reluctant to press further.

Such was not the case with Frank A. Daniels, Sr., president and publisher of *The News and Observer* in Raleigh. Described by Herbert as RTI's business conscience, as Gross was its scientific conscience, Daniels' own conscience must have been stirred by the inability to resolve this lingering issue. After all, agreement in principle had been stated and restated, and metes and bounds had been delineated to everyone's satisfaction. What remained was to get it done, precisely what Daniels determined to do. He made his purposeful way to Foundation officers Davis and Moore, securing their assent to conclude the matter and their cooperation in laying the case before Hodges.

It worked. On January 18, 1972, the Foundation announced its board's approval of Hodges' recommendation that the remaining 107 acres be donated to RTI in a single transfer. According to the Foundation's announcement, "Hodges said the action would in effect be a gift to the three Triangle Universities that own and control the Institute."

This happy conclusion to the campus tangle brought RTI's final resolution of appreciation and gratitude. Herbert forwarded it to Hodges on January 20, 1972, with a cover letter that ended "I want to express my thanks, and that of the Institute's staff, for the confidence which you and the other officers of the Foundation have demonstrated in the future of RTI."

Ironically, Herbert wrote to Hodges again the very next day about "the startling news of your retirement from the chairmanship of the Foundation. Your identification with the Research Triangle program, from the earliest spark of the idea to today's internationally recognized success, has been so close that it seems impossible to visualize the operation without you at the helm of the Foundation." Hodges died two years later at age 76.

II. Campus Development

A brief chronology of RTI's permanent buildings can begin with some that weren't. One was a tired old barn that both Foundation and Institute used for storage. Several other aged farm structures were beyond use or repair. Another was 1,200 square feet of unfinished, unpainted cement block without heat, water, septic tank, or interior doors. An RTI investment of $29,500 converted it into a small animal experimentation laboratory called the Mouse House. All of these, and a small pond by the barn, were in the path of Interstate 40's right of way.

A later structure also located on the southern portion of the campus was a meteorological field station consisting of a 120-foot aluminum air sampling tower, surface instrumentation, and a 350-square-foot building for data recording equipment. When the station began operating in February 1965 it marked RTI's entry into atmospheric chemistry research, 25 years later one of the Institute's major activities. The tower was one of the nation's first facilities for studying vertical gases in a rural environment. It, too, fell victim to I-40. Highway construction dust, roadbuilding equipment emissions, and later traffic fumes would render the sampling station scientifically valueless. It was dismantled in 1971, and eventually replaced by expanded and more versatile facilities for research on environmental measurement techniques.

Of the buildings that do exist, their order of occupancy began with the Bacon Street Annex, Hanes, and Dreyfus, as has been described. The annex and Hanes filled up rapidly, while Dreyfus, dedicated to polymer research, briefly housed the first three people in the new Geophysics Laboratory that started early in 1964.

So the 10,300 square feet in building 3 were the first real on-campus expansion space at management's disposal. The building's completion in 1963 temporarily relieved (space relief at RTI is always temporary) pressure at Bacon Street and in Hanes by providing quarters for the Operations Research Division and the Solid State Laboratory (see Chapter 12).

Origins of the Ragland Building (#4) have been described. In April 1965 the first occupants of its 34,000 square feet were measurements and controls offices on the ground floor and laboratories in the basement. Operations research and economics soon began filling up what was to become its half of the ground floor, joined by geophysics, radiation systems, and some of statistics which, a year and a half later, would occupy half of the ground floor. Basement space was assigned to or reserved for the computer center, switchboard, library, mail room, supply room, report editing, and technical illustrating. In building 3, the space vacated by ORE was occupied by the Natural Products Laboratory's pharmacology and toxicology groups, which moved from Bacon Street.

October 19, 1966, was a day of rejoicing, the long-awaited opening of a cafeteria in new building 5, a 10,300-square-foot twin of #3. Limited though its menu was to soup, salads, sandwiches, desserts, and beverages, the cafeteria was an instant success. Until then the staff brought lunch pails, brown bags, and thermos bottles, or relied on vending machines for sandwiches, crackers, candy bars, and soft drinks. The closest roadstand was halfway to Durham on highway 55. The closest place to entertain business guests was the Blair House restaurant, a long eight miles west between Durham and Chapel Hill on highway 15-501 just a couple of hundred yards from where University Tower now stands. The DeliBoxes, Triangle Squares, and fine hotel dining in and close to the Park were years away. RTI's cafeteria now serves breakfast and a variety of hot luncheon entrees.

Building 5's initial scientific residents were the radiation systems, measurement and controls, and geophysics laboratories, all of them moving from Ragland.

RTI/University cooperation was the cause for an acceleration in campus development. Building 6 was its effect. Completed only five months after #5, RTI built it for lease to the UNC School of Medicine. A National Institutes of Health grant of $17 million was creating a new UNC Center for Research in Pharmacology and Toxicology, but facilities in Chapel Hill had not progressed beyond early design stages, and it was urgent that work begin as soon as possible on basic research and training programs related to the rational use of drugs and their potential toxic properties. Facilities vice president Ashton had the building ready in February 1967. UNC's researchers and equipment remained there until December 1973, more than twice as long as anticipated, a stretch-out that severely hampered RTI. During this time the staff almost doubled to 465 and, despite having constructed and occupied three other new buildings, the Institute had been forced to rent offices in commercial buildings of the Foundation's Park Plaza service center along highway 54. Rentals there continue today to house international research and elements of biometrics research, computer science, and data services.

Building 7 was completed at the end of 1970 to absorb overflow from statistics and operations research in Ragland. The same size as its numbered predecessors, it completed a four-building mall.

The next summer chemistry and life sciences moved from Bacon Street into the Grover M. Hermann Laboratory Building, thanks to the gifts from Hermann and Watts Hill, and to mortgage financing.

Building 9 was completed in December 1972 and occupied at first by statistical and survey research overflow. Another 10,300-square-foot structure, but of slightly different design, it serves as a western anchor for the mall formed by 3, 5, 6, and 7.

Next came the George Watts Hill Building, whose 46,000 square feet provided welcome legroom and expansion space for social and statistical sciences. Moves into Hill commenced several months prior to dedication ceremonies, which took place on October 21, 1977, but four and one-half years after the architects' planning began. The long delay was due to design changes, one of which needs explanation.

Every nickel had always mattered at RTI, every expenditure was examined. There wasn't a frill in sight. For example, the only carpeting was in the office half of the newly refurbished Bacon Street Annex. (The Dreyfus lobby sported a rug inside the front doors.) Administrative staff members, the walls of their Hanes Building offices finished in uncompromising cinder block, were able but few, stretched thin as could be to carry out their duties. Buildings, furnishings, and administrative overhead alike were spared any embellishment that might deprive a scientist of needed research support or of a competitive edge in costing a proposal. Lean and Spartan is how RTI had to be at the start, and Herbert saw no reason not to keep it that way. This new five-story building, initially designated as #10, was to be designed accordingly.

Hill wasn't so sure. What he saw when #10's planning began in 1973 was an institute recognized far and wide not only for its own achievements but also for its role as the centerpiece of an unparalleled research park. He felt that this institute's appearance counted, that its looks should affirm success, that its president's office might have a carpet.

Hill was chairman of the board and chairman of the Building Committee and he argued the point with Herbert, but didn't insist. Instead, after it became clear he'd made no headway, he said that if Herbert would add a sixth floor for fully appointed RTI executive offices, he, Hill, would pay for it. After analyzing the obstacles and options for $1\frac{1}{2}$ seconds, Herbert said okay. (The Hill Building's lobby isn't carpeted, but everything else in it is. Retroactive carpeting later appeared throughout the Ragland Building's upper floor, in Hanes, and in many, but not all, office, conference, and library areas of the numbered buildings, Dreyfus, and Hermann.)

In October 1978 chemistry and life sciences' animal colony was enlarged by 8,900 square feet. The following summer a services building of 41,000 square feet and three small auxiliary buildings were completed for storage, supplies, shop, safety and security offices, print shop, mail room, graphic arts and, later, fitness rooms and aerosol technology research. In September 1979 the second half of the Dreyfus hollow square was completed with a 20,000-square-foot addition whose initial occupants were physical sciences, analytical chemistry, genetics, and several environmental sciences laboratories.

Design and financing arrangements were by then under way for a major new research resource, and in the spring of 1984 an innovative engineering sciences facility opened. RTI's semiannual meeting was held there in May, at which time Hobbs reported the decision that the building was to be named for George R. Herbert. Within just a couple of years the honoree had brought himself to call it by the right name nearly every time. The building has offices on two stories that curve along a 90-degree arc ending with laboratories for computer and systems sciences, and for semiconductor materials research and device fabrication. It also features a teleconferencing center that links RTI with CONCERT, a statewide video and data network that interconnects participating universities, industries, and the Institute with the MCNC Supercomputing Center's CRAY Y-MP.

The award of a five-year, $13 million chemical support contract from the National Toxicology Program was followed, in 1985, by completion of a materials handling structure and the start of another animal colony expansion.

At the May 1987 semiannual Board of Governors meeting, Herbert announced that Marcus E. Hobbs would be the name on RTI's newest building. At 52,000 square feet on four levels, it is the Institute's largest. It accommodates social, economic, educational, and policy research centers, plus elements of several environmental and engineering sciences centers. Another occupant is TULCo, the Triangle Universities Licensing Consortium, of which RTI is an affiliate.

September 28, 1989, was ribbon-cutting day at RTI's child day-care center, only the second such facility in the Research Triangle Park. Consisting of a 6,500-square-foot building and 8,000 square feet of playground, the center was constructed through Board of Governors appropriations totaling $579,000. The center is leased for one dollar a year to the separately incorporated RTI Parents Child Care Organization. Operations of the center, including staffing, are the PCCO's responsibility and are conducted on an entirely self-supporting basis through fees, fund raisers, and gifts.

Work is slated to begin in 1991 on a major chemistry laboratory building.

1 This May 1986 photograph is as close as anyone will come to a Research Triangle founders' portrait. Affiliations are given only for those who are not identified in the text.
Seated: Romeo H. Guest, Archie K. Davis, William C. Friday, George Watts Hill, George L. Simpson, Jr., and George R. Herbert.
Standing: William B. Aycock, UNC chancellor from 1957 to 1964; Dean W. Colvard; Robert E. Leak, who was president of the Research Triangle Foundation for a couple of years in the mid-1980s; Carey H. Bostian; Edward L. Rankin, private secretary to Governor Luther H. Hodges; John T. Caldwell, who succeeded Bostian as chancellor at N.C. State in 1959; Elizabeth J. Aycock; William F. Little; William D. Snider, editor emeritus of the *Greensboro Daily News;* William D. Stevenson; Arthur C. "Buck" Menius; Pearson H. Stewart; and Marcus E. Hobbs.

2

3

4

2 This photograph of George R. Herbert was published for the first time in December 1978. On that and several later occasions it was mis-captioned "RTI staff and facilities, January 1959." Rather, it was taken in the spring of that year by Samuel C. Ashton somewhere on the campus-to-be.

3 In 1984 Alva L. Finkner and Nancy Campbell Monroe celebrated the 25th anniversary of RTI project #1, which began on March 2, 1959.

4 Sam Ashton at the site of the first RTI laboratory building on Bacon Street in Durham, spring 1959.

5

5 George R. Herbert in 1959, his first year as Institute president. In 1989 he stepped aside to the new position of vice chairman and president emeritus.

6

7

6 The Camille Dreyfus Laboratory's first 20,000 square feet and its auditorium were dedicated in November 1961. The hollow square was completed in 1978 with addition of the second 20,000 square feet.

7 Gertrude M. Cox in her Hanes Building office in 1963 with Hale C. Sweeny.

8

9

8 Edgar A. Parsons, right, led RTI's civil defense research for nearly ten years. With him in 1963 are staff members Edward L. Hill, Philip S. McMullan, and William G. Howard. Hill was still at RTI in 1990 as senior administrative analyst in the office of the executive vice president.

9 At the Bacon Street annex in 1963, Charles L. "Les" Britt and Carl D. Parker inspect a 3-axis gyroscope with analog simulator. Both electrical engineers were still with RTI 27 years later.

10

11

10 Hugh W. Hunter, RTI's first research vice president, in his Hanes building office, 1964.

11 Vivian T. Stannett, associate director of the Camille Dreyfus Laboratory, in 1965.

12

13

12 RTI's Ralph L. Ely, Jr., was the coordinator and Duke University's Marcus E. Hobbs the chairman of a panel of scientific and health policy experts whose deliberations concerned plans and programs for what is now the National Institute of Environmental Health Sciences. Panel meetings took place in the Camille Dreyfus auditorium, where this photograph was taken in August 1965.

13 Luther H. Hodges and RTI board chairman George Watts Hill at the Ragland Building dedication in November 1965.

14

14 UNC president William C. Friday, left, visits with RTI's new research vice president, Chester W. Clark, in November 1965.

15 In Stockholm, Sweden, at the June 1966 annual meeting of the International Union of Pure and Applied Chemistry, the successful results of preliminary tests obtained with the anti-cancer compound camptothecin were first reported by Monroe E. Wall, second from right. Pictured with him later that summer were Institute senior chemists M. C. Wani, Keith H. Palmer, and C. Edgar Cook (who in 1983 succeeded Wall as RTI vice president for chemistry and life sciences.)

16 RTI's campus in 1967. Hanes Building front and center, Camille Dreyfus Laboratory and auditorium left center, and buildings #3 (mostly hidden by trees), #5, to the right, and #6 above them.
Jenkins Road led south from the Ragland Building, right center, past the sites of the present Hill, Hobbs, and Herbert buildings, past the pond and storage barn, and on to highway 54.
At upper right, Hill Drive, which connected 54 and Cornwallis Road, has since been replaced by the Durham Expressway.

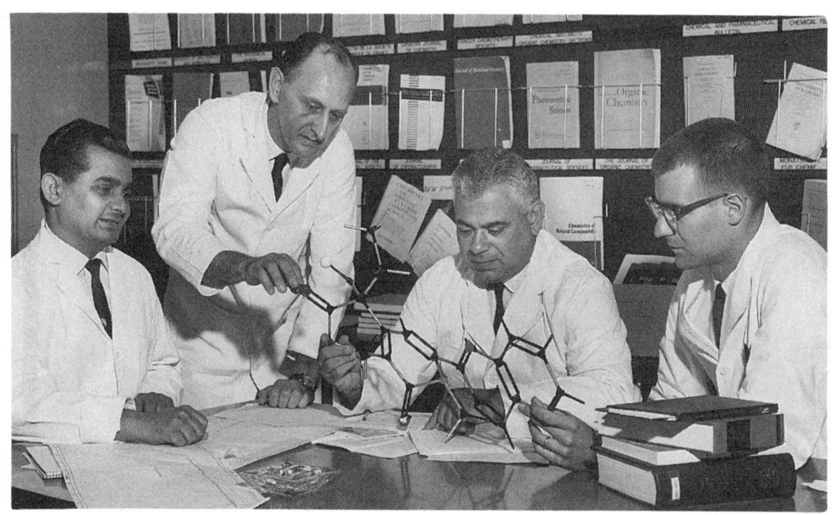

15

16

17

18

19

17 Among the major section authors of the 1967 Prentice-Hall book on *Fundamentals of Silicon Integrated Device Technology* were Robert P. Donovan, Bobby M. Berry and, seated, solid state research director Robert M. Burger. Also contributing to the volume's preparation were Sally Boyce, Linda Joyner and, at right, RTI report editor C. H. "Hu" Burnett.

18 William C. Eckerman, center, was the initial National Assessment of Educational Progress project leader and was succeeded by James R. Chromy, left. Both would become RTI research vice presidents. William K. Grogan served as survey operations manager in the field. Photograph made in February 1969.

19 In May 1969 Clifford E. Decker and Ronald B. Strong inspected an ozone intake tube during an oceanographic and meteorological experiment in the Caribbean Sea.

20

21

20 A garnish of Governors attended RTI's annual meeting in the Camille Dreyfus auditorium in November 1969. Luther H. Hodges, Dan K. Moore, incumbent Robert W. Scott, and Terry Sanford were all stalwart supporters of RTI, a tradition continued by their successors James E. Holshouser, Jr., and James B. Hunt, Jr.

21 RTI board chairman George Watts Hill, right, has annually hosted a luncheon for ten-year staff members. The first group, representing the decade 1959 – 1969, posed with him early in 1970. From left, they are George R. Herbert (11 years), Lewis H. Ballard, William H. Perkins, Jr., Ralph L. Ely, Jr., W. J. Thomas, Harold M. Richter, Samuel C. Ashton, Maxine Bondy, and Gertrude M. Cox. Inset: Alva L Finkner.

22

23

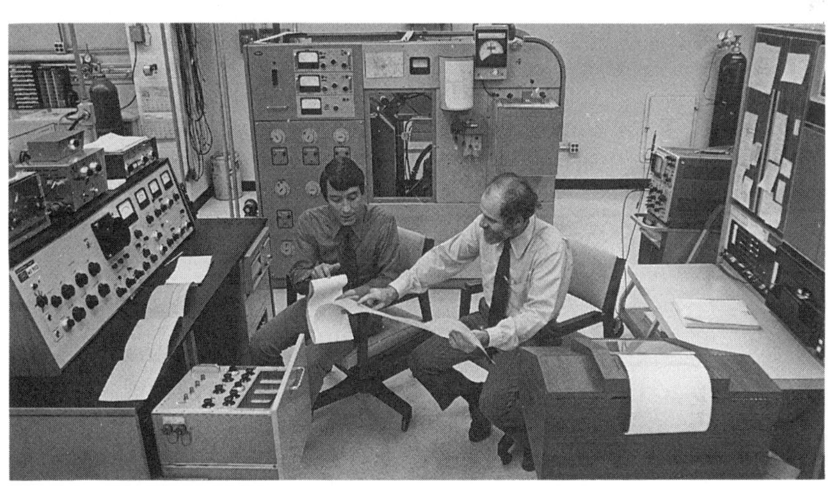

24

22 Anton Peterlin in the fall of 1970.

23 James J. B. Worth initiated RTI's environmental sciences research in 1964 and was elected a group vice president in 1971. With him in this 1970 photograph is Suzanne P. Nash, the Institute's corporate secretary since 1987.

24 For several years after the establishment of the Research Triangle Regional Mass Spectrometry Center, technician Fred P. Williams, left, was the most photographed individual at RTI. With him here in 1972 is center manager and assistant chemistry and life sciences director David W. Rosenthal, who described the mass spec as "the Supreme Court of small amounts."

25

26

25 In a 1974 photograph, James B. Tommerdahl alights from an EPA plane used for collecting air samples from various locations. The mechanisms that transport pollutants from metropolitan areas to create high ozone concentrations in rural sections have been the subject of extensive RTI studies. Tommerdahl became an RTI research vice president in 1983.

26 RTI's tenth building was named for Board of Governors chairman George Watts Hill, center. With him in this 1975 photograph near the building's site were treasurer William H. Perkins, Jr., vice president Samuel C. Ashton, president George R. Herbert, and board Executive Committee chairman William F. Little who was then vice chancellor of the University of North Carolina at Chapel Hill.

27

28

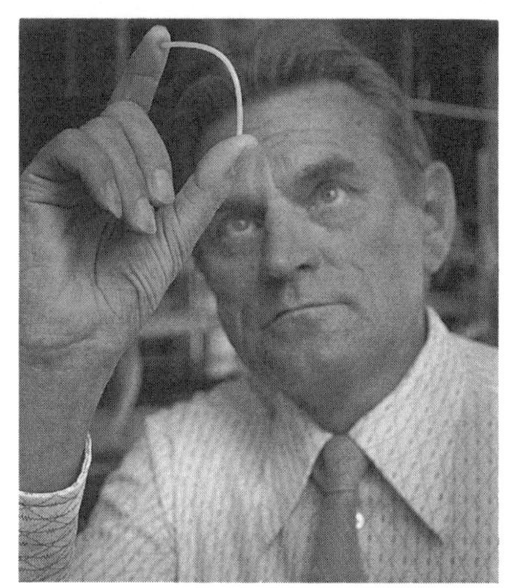

29

27 RTI's four research vice presidents in February 1976 were William C. Eckerman, Daniel G. Horvitz, James J. B. Worth, and Monroe E. Wall.

28 Philip Abraham, George H. Dunteman, and Blake S. Wilson were the winners of RTI's first Professional Development Awards in 1977. They are shown here on one of the islands that dotted the pool surrounding the Camille Dreyfus auditorium. Also, the pool was plagued by leaks, and repairs were costly, so in 1985 it was covered with a wooden patio.

29 In 1976 Anton Schindler demonstrated the flexibility of the polymer material used for RTI's biodegradable contraceptive implant.

30

30 As executive director of the Research Triangle Committee, George L. Simpson, Jr., right, made contributions to RTI and to the entire Research Triangle enterprise that have not been surpassed. He spoke at the Institute's twentieth annual meeting in November 1978 and is shown here at that time with Daniel G. Horvitz, who was then RTI vice president for statistical sciences.

31 Robert T. Armstrong in November 1978. A member of the original Research Triangle Committee and a founding and Lifetime Member of RTI's Board of Governors, his role in propelling RTI onto the international scientific stage is described in Chapter 7.

32 Lois A. MacGillivray left RTI near the end of 1981 to become president of Holy Names College. Succeeding her as director of the Center for Population and Urban-Rural Studies was Ronald W. Johnson, who became an RTI vice president two years later.

31

32

33

34

33 Paul M. Gross and Marcus E. Hobbs, chemistry professors and senior administrative officers at Duke University, both hold places of highest honor in RTI annals. They pose here in the Camille Dreyfus Laboratory courtyard in 1984 after receiving recognition for 25 years of service on the RTI Board of Governors and the board's Executive Committee. Hobbs was committee chairman from 1962 to 1969 and again from 1977 until the present.

34 On a year-long World Bank assignment to the Kingdom of Nepal in 1985, James S. McCullough, left, head of the Office for International Studies, and Tom Steubner helped local officials strengthen municipal financial management practices.

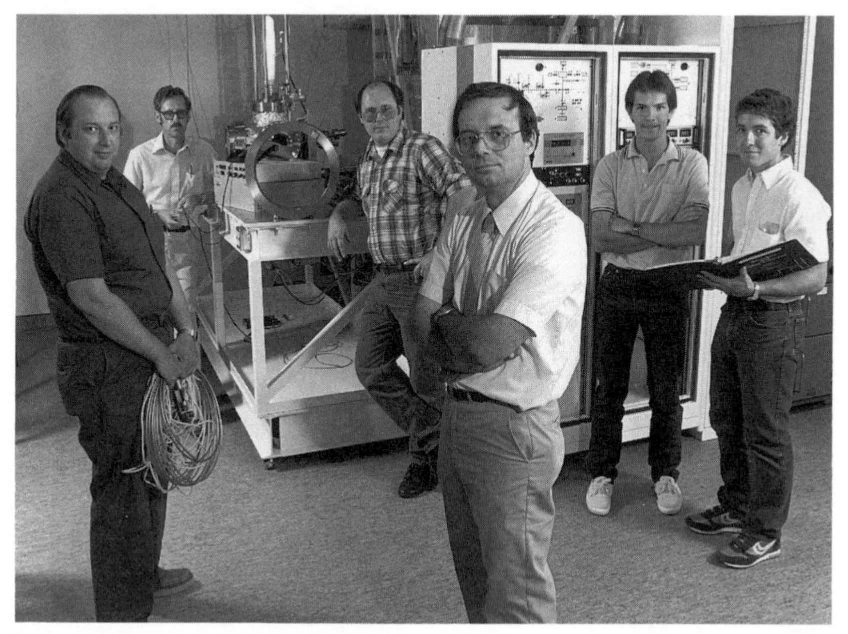

35

35 R&D on new types of semiconductor materials and devices has won international prominence for RTI. In this 1985 photograph, semiconductor devices research manager Robert J. Markunas, foreground, and his colleagues are shown soon after the successful trial run of the plasma-enhanced chemical vapor deposition reactor that they designed and built. Standing with him, from left, are Roger A. Connor, A. Dean Brooks, Robert C. Hendry, George C. Hudson, and G. Gill Fountain.

36

36 Technology applications director Doris J. Rouse posed in June 1986 with two earlier heads of the Biomedical Applications Team, James N. Brown, Jr., an Institute chief scientist, and F. Thomas Wooten, who was vice president for electronics and systems research and who became RTI's president in October 1989.

37

37 Senior researchers in on the start of RTI's five-year study of the effects that U.S. Army family assistance programs have on soldier retention and readiness included, in this January 1987 photograph, Barbara A. Moser, Robert M. Bray, Janet D. Griffith, J. Valley Rachal and, seated, Alvin M. Cruze, who in January 1989 succeeded Dan Horvitz as executive vice president.

12. Into the Sixties

This starts a series of four chapters that cover, however sketchily, RTI's research and organizational development over nearly three decades to the end of 1989. It's a good place to state some reservations.

No history can pretend to be wholly complete or completely objective. The three decades have been crammed with technically complex activities of endless variety carried out by researchers representing scores of disciplines and interests. In the pages that follow, most research and nearly all researchers are inevitably left out.

If it's hard to tell where environmental concerns end and health concerns begin, it would be infinitely harder to tell in detail about Institute research in these two fields, far and away RTI's major endeavors. The Department of Health and Human Services and the EPA provide by far the biggest portions of RTI revenue, but health and environmental research also account for much of RTI's work for private-sector clients, the Department of Defense, NASA, and the U.S. Agency for International Development.

Health and environment alone, not counting other projects in the social sciences, chemistry, and engineering, have involved hundreds of separate studies and hundreds of research personnel scattered through twenty multidisciplinary centers. Selectivity and a broad brush have been called for. Judgments have had to be made.

Appendix II conveys, in brief compass, the sense and the fact that RTI's specialty is diversity. Were anything close to a comprehensive discourse upon all topics possible, its technical complexities would be very nearly unreadable. Anyway, as British historian Lytton Strachey observed, "Omission is the beginning of all art."

The foregoing paragraphs are offered in explanation. They may also do double duty as apology, should anybody want one.

Reliability

At the very first Board of Governors annual business meeting, held at Bacon Street on November 4, 1959, Herbert raised a fundamental question and pointed in the direction of an answer: "How are we to identify research areas sufficiently new, or only emerging into national importance, that are not completely staked out by older organizations? To succeed, a new institute needs to develop some areas of unique strength in order to have a chance to make significant contributions and build its reputation."

Unique strengths were implicit in the personnel and projects inherited from the Institute of Statistics, and in the previous week's announcement of the Dreyfus Foundation's memorial grant for a polymer research laboratory. The search for the new and the important, if not necessarily the unique, succeeded throughout RTI's first decade in laying a foundation for growth and diversity to come. Engineering reliability led the way.

Two reliability studies have been mentioned in Chapter 1 and Chapter 8, both for Bell Telephone Laboratories. The first, completed in September 1959, was a small one, a $4,000 carryover from the Institute of Statistics. The second, valued at $170,897 and ending in June 1963, was to develop statistical methods for evaluating the reliability of the Nike missile's digital logic systems.

Such were the beginnings of what is today RTI's acknowledged expertise in reliability-related programs such as fault-tolerant avionic systems, airborne navigational aids, spacecraft launch safety, computer assurance, and environmental quality assurance.

Electronic equipment reliability concerns were, and are, both economic and operational. Even at the start of the '60s, for example, military and space agency costs for maintenance and repair to avoid or overcome reliability failures were in the billions of dollars annually. Of particular operational importance was, and is, the potential loss of service should systems fail at times when national security or human safety are endangered.

In their plans for what would be RTI's Statistics Research Division, Gertrude Cox and Al Finkner provided for an engineering section that would include research on probability theory and systems performance prediction. Along with Bell Labs, the U.S. Army was an early client in these fields. The terms "reliability" and "NASA" appear nowhere in the 1958 Cox report or in Finkner's notes and records, yet reliability research is the topic that began a contractual relationship between RTI and NASA that has existed continuously since 1961.

First chronologically was the contract to prepare *Reliability Abstracts and Technical Reviews*, a monthly publication that RTI generated for nine years until NASA discontinued it in 1970. RATR provided appraisals of the quality and usefulness of reliability research and testing that were reported in English-language technical literature. Statisticians and engineers at RTI and from State, Duke, and UNC participated in document selection, analysis, abstracting, and review.

The publication was important for both NASA and RTI, but comparatively small game. Cox had far more ambitious things in mind: (1) develop composite probabilistic modeling techniques to enhance the reliability of components, devices, and systems used in NASA space missions, and (2) test these techniques on existing astronautic systems.

Cox had the plans and she had the wherewithal, too, in terms of talent at hand for new statistical designs for conducting experiments, for the control and optimization of complex physical systems, for probability theory, and for statistical sampling innovations.

The problem would lie in getting NASA's attention. Cox had mentioned her ideas in a brief conversation with NASA administrator James E. Webb, but a considerably more substantial push was needed. Paul Gross took care of it. He arranged for himself, Cox, and Herbert to meet with his friend Webb in mid-June 1961. That same afternoon the visitors from RTI submitted their proposal to NASA scientists and left confident that it would be given careful review.

This project on the functional analysis of systems succeeded in making a substantial contribution to an area of vital concern to NASA, and in other ways as well. Foremost among them was the demonstration to NASA officials, and to others, that scientists at the unknown Research Triangle Institute somewhere in North Carolina could take on and solve problems of the most abstruse technical nature. It was, obviously, good for RTI to have NASA know this, as it was also good for others to know it. Some particular others, all at top universities and all but one of them previously ignorant of RTI, were six blue ribbon scientists (one of them a Nobel laureate) corraled by Gross from the U.S. and Europe as a project advisory committee, which he chaired. RTI benefited from having the committee members know about its capabilities and about Paul Gross's personal interest in it.

Something else that it was good for RTI to have NASA and the advisory committee know about was Harald Cramer, who held two one-year-apart appointments to the project research team. A great friend of Cox's and perhaps the leading international authority on probability theory, Cramer was former president of the University of Stockholm and had recently retired as chancellor of all universities in Sweden. RTI kept good company.

Minneapolis-Honeywell's Centaur inertial guidance system was selected as the specific vehicle for demonstrating the application of RTI's probabilistic model. The tests completely confirmed its effectiveness, accuracy, and reliability.

Civil Defense

Soon after taking office in January 1961, President Kennedy's administration began emphasizing the need for increased attention to emergency planning and civil defense research. The recent shooting down of an American U-2 reconnaissance plane over Soviet territory, and the subsequent cancellation of an Eisenhower-Khrushchev summit meeting in Paris, had dangerously lowered the temperature of the cold war. It was soon to grow even colder with erection of the Berlin wall, and then drop to a freezing crisis with delivery of Soviet missiles to Cuba. As international tensions heightened, the threat of nuclear arms exchange grew. Nobody wanted to think about it, but they had to. At the President's urging, homeowners and institutions began building and stocking bombshelters.

Except for the employees of a small government bureau no one had ever heard of, civil defense research was, in contrast with the armed forces' well-publicized preparedness measures, pretty much a new ball game. Very few people knew it existed, or that funding for the interstate highway system, inaugurated in 1956, had been justified largely in terms of civil and military defense.

The President's new priority opened up an inviting field for a fledgling research institute, especially inviting because it was level and open, not staked out by others. If RTI didn't have a civil defense research track record, neither had anyone else. But what RTI did have as a special asset was operations research director Bud Parsons, whose previous position had been a dual one as chief of economics research and deputy chief of operations research with the federal Office of Civil Defense and Mobilization.

From the time of his arrival at RTI in October 1960, Parsons had intended to cultivate his former Office of Civil Defense (OCD) associates as clients. His chances weren't hurt by the new administration's policy of greater emphasis on protection of civilian populations during a national emergency. Early in 1961, after securing modest contracts for a fallout shelter analysis plan and for evaluating shelter elements in building construction plans, he garnered a wide-ranging, $620,000, three-year OCD project package.

Over the next decade RTI won a place among the top research contractors for the OCD and other agencies concerned with emergency preparedness and post-attack recovery. Those others were the U.S. Public Health Services, Federal Power Commission, Air Force, and Navy.

The Operations Research Division, later Operations Research and Economics (ORE), performed on some sixty separate civil defense contracts, many of them with multiple tasks, which was then the largest number of RTI projects in a single category. By the time Parsons left the Institute in 1969, civil defense work also accounted for the largest number of cumulative revenue dollars, four and a half million of them.

Other, and much smaller, segments of ORE revenue were from research in human resource development and labor economics, marketing and distribution, military systems, nursing home operations and costs, regional economics, and community health services delivery effectiveness at maternal and infant care clinics.

Thirty years later it is difficult to call to mind the conditions and attitudes that led to a national priority for civil defense. Yet the dangers, the fears, were real enough. Civil defense research went a long way toward extending RTI's multidisciplinary capabilities, and several ORE researchers went on to senior Institute positions. Physicist Fred A. Bryan, Jr., is director of the Center for Epidemiologic and Medical Studies, for example, with biologist and health analyst Benjamin S. H. Harris III as assistant center director in the Washington, D.C., office. Industrial engineer Edward L. Hill is senior administrative analyst in the office of the executive vice president; Robert H. Thornton, trained in chemistry and mathematics, is director of the Center for Computer Science; civil engineer Deane F. Tolman became director of environmental systems research; James C. Wright, a data processing engineer, heads the Ragland Computer Center; economist Alvin M. Cruze is executive vice president.

Versatility marked civil defense research resources. A head count made near the end of 1968 showed 55 professional staff members with 108 degrees in 47 subject fields ranging from aeronautical engineering to zoology. This diversity came together in a common systems analysis and computer capability that remains today a conspicuous feature throughout all RTI operations. One case in point, specific to civil defense research, was an analytical nuclear casualty estimation technique developed by Philip S. McMullan and other analysts. By combining a number of analytical models into a single program, it estimated target damage and potential weapons effects by simulating scores of combinations of circumstances from topographic data and population density to aiming error probability and wind velocity.

Complexity marked civil defense research methods. Planning for human protection and survival during and after nuclear attack involved a bewildering array of speculative and provisional circumstances, all possible in greater or lesser degree. Subjects of relevance dealt with virtually every consideration that would confront the civilian populace: shielding from blast and radiation, shelter from fallout, safe supplies of food and water and medicines, population movement routes, damage control, communications, sanitation, housing, clothing, disease prevention, social order, political stability, fire suppression, decontamination, and a thousand and one other environmental, geographic, economic, and behavioral variables.

If a confrontation of world powers should dissolve into an attack situation, the researchers postulated that preparedness planning would lead, first, to the activation of warning systems in place throughout the country and next, military countermeasures aside, in the movement of populations to shelter. Shelter is the essence of protection, and is also the single subject in which RTI contributed most significantly to OCD research and planning. Notable would be work on shelter surveys, preparation, and engineering led by Ed Hill, and radiation shielding research directed by Bryan.

Any cover at all would be preferable to none, but RTI demonstrated that adequate shelter hinged not only on numerous structural features of a given building, but on a swarm of other factors as well: the ease of getting to the building and finding its shelter area; the shelter's location relative both to population concentration and to probable attack effects; how many people it could accommodate and for how long.

Researchers at RTI and other OCD contractors knew well enough that their conclusions and preparations were ultimately testable only in an event that would occur but once. Short of that carnage, however, peacetime emergencies—floods, hurricanes, forest fires, earthquakes, blizzards—provided performance measures for evaluating their work in relief and rehabilitation planning, communications systems, and evacuation and rescue techniques.

Beyond its service to the nation's preparedness and thus to its strategic deterrent stance, civil defense research was important to RTI in terms of multidisciplinary staff acquisition, revenue growth, and recognition by federal agencies. While acknowledging its timely contributions to RTI's success, other initiatives and capabilities introduced in the 1960s were to have even longer-lasting influence on the Institute's evolving shape and substance.

Semiconductors

February 26, 1962, is a date that George Herbert points to with unblushing pride as the day that Robert M. Burger joined RTI and that microelectronics research came to North Carolina. Not quite right on the second count, but the confluence of those pairings was to have a profound effect on each and, as it turned out, on space, defense, energy, and industrial research advances as well.

Six months earlier, research vice president Hugh Hunter had written that "In connection with [the] . . . manufacture of electronic components, Corning Glass Works has asked RTI to establish a group to do research on their film technology relating to micro-electronics. . . . We are preparing a formal proposal and have been significantly aided by a group in the Electrical Engineering Department at Duke University."* The invaluable university connection again, nowhere to be more visible and noteworthy than in the engineering sciences.

By the time Burger arrived at RTI's Bacon Street annex, the proposal to Corning had been accepted and the project was in Ralph Ely's freshly renamed Measurements and Controls Laboratory, where a separate thin films study for Western Electric was nearly completed.

Burger took over supervision of the Corning project on thin film capacitors. Almost at once he also found himself in demand as a contributor to the Statistics Research Division's reliability projects, which needed strong engineering and physics support. This was just what Burger could supply, with his physics Ph.D. from Brown University and his several years with Westinghouse in molecular electronics.

Molecular electronics is what civilian scientist Richard D. Alberts was in charge of for the Air Force Systems Command at Wright-Patterson Air Force Base (WPAFB) in Ohio, the USAF's principal R&D center, and it was he who gave RTI Burger's name and recommended him. (Alberts is one of the genuine pioneers in the world of semiconductor science. He became plans director of the Avionics Laboratory at Wright-Patterson, and after retiring in 1975 he joined RTI for eight years.)

In the summer of 1962 Burger and Hunter had completed their plans for a Solid State Laboratory (SSL) for Burger to head. Joined a year later by N.C. State's Electrical Engineering Department, SSL provided the initial impetus for the expansion of microelectronics R&D enterprise in the Research Triangle. This RTI/NCSU collaboration merits later comment, but Duke's early semiconductor contribution should be mentioned now, for among Burger's most notable recruiting successes were several electrical engineers who came to RTI through the university's graduate program in solid state electronics. Some, like the very first three—Jimmie J. Wortman, Larry K. Monteith, Allie M. Smith—went on to glistening academic careers. Another early solid state star, physicist Robert P. Donovan, came to RTI from Westinghouse soon after Burger did in 1962 and is today a clean-room contamination and particle-measurement authority in the Center for Aerosol Technology. Two others of the current staff, James N. Brown, Jr., and Mayrant Simons, Jr., are also products of the Duke Ph.D. program who joined RTI in 1964 and 1966, respectively.

In 1962, integrated circuits—more complex than transistors, and also lighter, smaller, cheaper, more reliable—were beginning to define new bound-

* One member of the group, a graduate student, was misidentified by Hunter as Frank Wooton instead of F. Thomas Wooten. He received his Ph.D. in 1964 and unsuccessfully applied to Burger for a job. He tried again two years later and this time Burger hired him for the solid state processing laboratory. In 1989 Wooten became RTI's second president.

aries for electronics, boundaries across which Burger's Solid State Laboratory led RTI and the Triangle area. Led more than that, for SSL's classic engineering series *Fundamentals of Silicon Integrated Device Technology,* or SIDT, was a publishing success from the start, becoming a standard reference in the field, and delivering exactly what its title promised to scientists in industry, government, and university laboratories. For many years Burger and the others enjoyed seeing copies of their work on display in other people's offices and laboratories wherever they went. One reason for its long-lived value is the emphasis on the "Fundamentals" of the title, the mathematics and basic physics rather than the flashier "Technology."

Produced under sponsorship of the Air Force Avionics Laboratory at WPAFB, the 16-part series on silicon integrated device theory, design, fabrication, and application was updated for publication in book form. Burger and Donovan were the editors of two Prentice-Hall volumes in 1967 and 1968.

Earlier, in 1965, NASA had published and given wide circulation to another Solid State Laboratory effort, *Microelectronics in Space Research*, written by Burger, Bobby M. Berry, and Monteith. Intended as part of a NASA program to spur industrial uses of microelectronic devices, the 130-page document identified SIDT as the technique that held the greatest potential for commercial development.

Burger and Solid State Laboratory engineers were by then combining with research statisticians to bring RTI a national reputation for their work with NASA on the behavior of electronic parts and devices, and their integration and performance within aerospace operating systems.

In addition to system and device reliability and microelectronic processes, the Solid State Laboratory had, within three years after its formation, expanded into basic and applied research on gas source impurity diffusion, device design theory, and electrochemical processes, and into the development of sensors for medical research and for micrometeoroids in space.

(Micrometeoroid detectors developed by RTI electrical engineers Carl D. Parker, Wortman, and others were aboard Pioneer 10 and Pioneer 11 when the spacecraft left Earth in 1972 and 1973 on their journeys across the asteroid belt to Jupiter, Saturn, and beyond. A later detector, fabricated by RTI's S. Ray Stilley and J. Harold White, and part of a dust-measurement experiment in which State's Wortman and Monteith were among the principals, was aboard NASA's long duration exposure facility (LDEF) when it went into orbit in April 1984 and when it was retrieved in January 1990 by the shuttle Columbia.)

Along with the Solid State Laboratory, the Radiation Systems Laboratory was a forerunner to RTI's later generations of noteworthy skills in the engineering sciences. RSL got under way in the summer of 1963. Equally descriptive names would have been Radio Frequency Laboratory or Antenna Laboratory, for its research dealt with communications, radar, navigation, and guidance and control systems. Basic work included electromagnetic theory and circuit theory. Applied projects were studies directed to wave propagation, antennas, microwave devices, and information displays. RSL's director throughout most of its four-year life was P. Gene Smith, a radar systems specialist. P. Gene lost little time in adding spice to RTI's payroll operations. His first professional recruit was A. Gene Smith.

Environmental Research

Air pollution was recognized as a nuisance by the late 1940s, but initial cares were pretty much limited to smog's annoying effects in Los Angeles. For many people, the beginning of the environmental movement wasn't until June 16, 1962. It was on that date that *The New Yorker* magazine published its first installment of Rachel Carson's *Silent Spring*, the book that was to raise public consciousness about environmental hazards to the crusade level, and whose momentum still energizes concerns about clean air, clean water, preservation, and waste disposal.

RTI's attention to these problems over the years has intensified and broadened to the extent that by 1990 the Institute is solidly established as an innovative, reliable environmental research contractor for federal agencies, state governments, and industry. As with other quality-of-life issues, RTI commits the full range of its multidisciplinary resources—in chemistry, economics, geology and hydrogeology, survey statistics, toxicology, meteorology, the engineering and computer sciences—to environmental research, primarily for the EPA, but also for the National Institutes of Health, Department of Defense, corporate clients, and industry associations.

Back in 1962 RTI had, with its habitual instinct for national priorities, completed its first environmental assignment, project #60*, designing the sample for a Public Health Service survey of public attitudes about threats from air pollution.

Most of the Institute's early environmental projects weren't directed to health effects, abatement strategies, or reliable methods for measuring pollutant levels, but dealt instead with earth-ocean-atmosphere interactions and physical phenomena: factors affecting ozone concentrations in the lower troposphere was the subject of one project, for example. For the U.S.

* Project #1, the Nashville morbidity survey, doesn't count. Although completed by RTI, the research was started by the Institute of Statistics. See Chapter 1.

Department of Commerce RTI developed an oceanographic data logging system, for the Air Force it aided in developing numerical and operational weather forecast procedures.

These and related studies were carried out in the Geophysics Laboratory, which was created as RTI's eighth research unit soon after the arrival of James J. B. Worth in March 1964. Town and gown in Chapel Hill were closely involved. Late the previous year Hugh Hunter had started a one-geologist Earth Sciences Division to work with UNC's Department of Geology on a successful proposal to an Air Force electronic systems unit for a study on the seismicity of the southeastern U.S. Hearing of RTI's need for a senior researcher to manage this project and secure others, a Chapel Hill businessman recommended his son's friend, Jim Worth. A meteorologist, Worth had for eight years been with Bendix Systems in Ann Arbor, Michigan, where he was senior manager for studies of atmospheric environments and their effects on instrumentation systems in satellite and rocket-propelled vehicles.

Within a year Worth had a small staff and modest programs in geology, meteorology, oceanography, and aerology. He was also working the university connection. Under the Air Force contract, for example, the seismograph and related sensors for detecting deep earth tremors were installed and maintained in UNC's geology building. Upon completion of the project at the end of 1966, title to the equipment passed to the university.

A National Science Foundation grant to UNC was soon to foster an even stronger tie between RTI and the university's Department of Environmental Sciences and Engineering. Under subcontract from UNC, the Institute bought the department's 120-foot air sampling tower (see Chapter 11) and moved it from Chapel Hill to be the major element in RTI's meteorological field station. The subcontract relationship accomplished more than that: it brought Lyman A. Ripperton and RTI together.

Worth remembers the station as being rudimentary, but despite its nonsophistication it enabled him and Ripperton to demonstrate the first workable techniques for bringing atmospheric gases from heights of 120 feet, 60 feet, 30 feet, and 4 feet to the surface, and for analyzing their behavior at each level. Ripperton was among the world's leading specialists in studies of the mechanism by which ozone and its precursors are transported from urban centers to create pollution concentrations in rural areas. For 15 years a UNC professor of environmental sciences, he was also an RTI consultant and became a member of the full-time staff in 1973, serving until his death five years later. Ripperton's instructional program became the model for similar activities at many universities, and Worth credits him with major responsibility for establishing RTI's reputation in environmental research.

UNC wasn't the only educational institution helping to foster RTI's programs in atmospheric sciences. Worth and James R. Smith of geophysics and Jim Tommerdahl of radiation systems led an RTI team that installed a comprehensive data logging system aboard the Eastward, the Duke Marine Laboratory's research vessel berthed at Beaufort, N.C. From masthead to keel and from bowsprit to afterdeck, they strung hundreds of feet of cable for operating an array of sensing devices from which a continuous sampling of 24 different parameters at the air-sea interface was recorded. Part of a weather analysis and prediction study for the U.S. Department of Commerce, RTI's data collection system ran during the Eastward's days at sea over a two-year period.

A few years later similar but more varied sensors were aboard the Cape Fear Technical Institute's SS Advance II for a 46-day scientific voyage from Wilmington to the Caribbean and on to the equator. They were part of a huge $22 million, summer-long experiment that involved 3 nations (U.S., Canada, Barbados), 10 federal agencies, 19 universities, 7 other research organizations, 10 ships, 24 aircraft, and thousands of weather balloons. RTI's corner of the project was small but significant. Meteorologist Smith and electronics engineer Tommerdahl were joined by atmospheric chemist Clifford E. Decker in designing and installing instrumentation that would sense and record not only weather data at and around the infinitesimally small but very real boundary, or interface, where sea and air meet, but also the temperature and salinity of seawater samples from the surface to depths of 2,000 meters, and the concentrations and distributions of properties such as ozone, nitrogen dioxide, and nitrogen oxide gases.

Organization

Establishment of the Geophysics Laboratory in early 1964 completed the eight-unit research organization that was to remain essentially unchanged for three and a half years, which is a longish time as RTI measures such things. "Essentially unchanged" is one way of saying there were changes. Some were of the organizational chart box variety, some were of the whose-name-is-new-in-the-box variety, and some are worth a mention here.

John C. Orcutt and Forest O. Mixon, both chemical engineers, joined the Statistics Research Division in early 1961 and 1962, respectively, and from 1963 to 1965 they were a two-person Rate Processes Group reporting to Hunter. Their work concentrated on process simulation, process optimization, and process controls, and later on it was they who undertook RTI's first theoretical and applied engineering research on sewage treatments and waste disposal techniques.

In the spring of 1965 they transferred to the Measurements and Controls Laboratory, with Orcutt as director, when Ralph Ely became a one-man office of Industry Services to offer technical assistance to North Carolina companies.* (Orcutt was manager of environmental engineering when he left RTI shortly after receiving his ten-year pin. Mixon was elected RTI vice president for chemical engineering in 1983. At the time of his death six years later, in a commercial airline crash, he was chief scientist and had spent 27 years with the Institute.)

Despite Herbert's preference for delaying until pressure turned to pain, it was after less than three years of operation that he had to concede that he, Perkins, Ashton, Hunter, and buyer W. J. Thomas were unable to carry the administrative load alone. They'd done it since early 1959, but by the fall of 1961 annual revenue had almost quintupled to $682,000, permanent staff had risen to 82, and the task of looking after both today's business and tomorrow's opportunities was getting beyond them. It was then that James R. Pearson came to help with a variety of duties, primarily project development and promotion. Late the following year he relieved chief accountant Perkins of contract administration responsibilities while staying active in technical marketing. By that time annual revenue had more than doubled to $1.4 million and staff numbered 131. In the summer of 1963 Robert M. Graper arrived to take a new position concerned with personnel administration and security matters. That fall, RTI's official numbers were $2.2 million in revenue and a staff of 174. Graper is still head of the Office of Human Resources and at the end of 1989 RTI's total staff was 1,499 and its revenue for the year was $88.3 million, climbing to $100.2 million in 1990.

In the summer of 1964 Cox took retirement a year early and became a part-time consultant to Finkner, who succeeded her as Statistics Research Division director.

In the fall Hunter announced his resignation, effective in March 1965, to return to California as research director of the Naval Ordnance Testing Station at China Lake. He and Herbert had amply demonstrated their resourcefulness in identifying promising fields of research and able scientists to cultivate them. Herbert's task now would be to find a replacement for his senior scientific officer, a vice president to lead RTI into its second generation of research operations.

* Later in the year and into 1966, Ely was coordinator of a Public Health Service project under which RTI assembled a panel of nationally known experts, planned their activities, conducted their meetings, which were held at RTI, and reported their recommendations concerning the feasibility of establishing what is now the National Institute of Environmental Health Sciences. The panel's chairman was Marcus Hobbs.

It wasn't all that difficult, thanks to the ever-present, ever-deepening university connection, this time with Duke chemist Marcus Hobbs, who was doing double duty as dean of the university and chairman of RTI's Executive Committee. The timing of Hunter's departure was practically perfect for his successor, Chester W. Clark, who had already written to Hobbs and Paul Gross about his desire for a change of scene. Hobbs, Gross, and others at Duke were well acquainted with Clark, a low temperature physicist with degrees from the University of California, a Ph.D. from the University of Leiden in the Netherlands, and a 35-year professional career devoted largely to scientific R&D endeavors. Clark's qualifications seemed unbeatable. Hobbs responded to his letter with a long distance telephone call, and in February 1965 Herbert flew off to see him at U.S. Army headquarters in Japan, where Clark was the two-star commanding general. Their visit went well, Herbert returned home to discuss terms of an offer with his board and senior staff, and Clark agreed to report for duty at RTI in August.

Clark deserves an adjective, maybe two. Far from being prideful, indeed he is the soul of modesty and seemliness, he nevertheless takes great pride in his role in creating what he likes to call "the O-th, or Zero-th, research organization in the Research Triangle." Predating RTI by years was the Army's Office of Ordnance Research, a Clark project for which planning had begun during the four years he was assistant director for Army ballistics research at the Aberdeen Proving Grounds in Maryland. (Among the posts Clark held before becoming major general in command of all U.S. Army forces in Japan, the most recent had been a Pentagon tour as director of Army R&D.)

The Office of Ordnance Research (OOR), later called the Army Research Office (ARO), has sponsored and coordinated basic research in the physical, biological, earth, and mathematical sciences. The work is carried out mostly under grants to universities and other research centers. The office began operations in June 1951; Marcus Hobbs was temporarily its chief scientist. Until moving to the Research Triangle Park in 1975, ARO was housed at Duke, where Hobbs and Gross were among the university scientists who had worked with Army officials, Clark very prominently, in establishing it. Their close involvements with RTI were persuasive factors in Clark's decision, and there were other local associations, too. For one thing, both of his children were Duke graduates, and another was the extent of his acquaintanceship with members of Duke's faculty and with OOR/ARO staff members. Among the latter was Grace C. Boddie, who would later become RTI vice president and senior counsel. Until joining the Institute in 1972, she was the ARO's comptroller and chief of research support management.

Clark's arrival at RTI was as a scientist and executive, not as a retired major general whose friendships and influence within the Department of

Defense might be instrumental in securing contract funding for the Institute. This didn't happen because it couldn't happen; neither Clark's nor Herbert's code of conduct let them play the game that way.

Up To BAT

A 1970 NASA publication about *Medical Benefits From Space Research* discussed four that originated with RTI, including electrodes painted on the skin for use in muscle therapy, an aerospace valve for urinary control, improved imagery for heart research, and a radiation probe for cancer research. The editor had more than fifty RTI "benefits" to choose from, all of them produced during what was then the four-year life of the Institute's Biomedical Applications Team, BATeam for short.

In June 1966, when Jim Brown of the Solid State Laboratory sold RTI's biomedical technology transfer capabilities to NASA, the Institute's new BATeam was one of seven similar teams that were created to help fulfill the agency's mandate, stipulated by Congress, to see to it that the new technologies developed for space exploration were also used for the public's direct benefit.

Brown had no way of knowing that a record for project longevity at RTI had started (1966-1990, and still active). He had no way of knowing that RTI's program would be the sole survivor of the original seven, or that in the early 1980s its scope would expand significantly under the more inclusive appellation of Technology Applications Team. Whether called BAT or TAT, the teams' successes are counted in the hundreds and range from information transfers to adaptive engineering, field testing, and product licensing.

The reasoning, valid still, behind NASA's technology utilization program, which has overseen BATeam and TATeam, was that America's aerospace effort was producing an enormously expanded technological base with the potential for being applied to a vast complex of problems which might otherwise appear quite unrelated to aerospace interests. In establishing NASA through the Space Act of 1958, Congress specifically directed the agency to search for such secondary applications, or technological spin-offs.

Specific to BATeam concerns, the key initial role for RTI was as an interface between space engineering and systems analysis on the one hand, and medical specialties on the other. "They have different vocabularies, experiences, and approaches," Brown said, "and it was our job to be the catalyst in finding a common ground for bringing them together to define medical problems and then to search for leads to possible solutions through NASA data banks and research centers."

Space-generated solutions to medical diagnostic and treatment problems have been many and varied. A handful from the BATeam's earlier years: (1) biological isolation garments were adapted to protect patients whose immune system deficiencies make them highly susceptible to infectious diseases. The original garments were worn by Apollo astronauts during the quarantine period after their return from the moon; (2) a stretchable helmet with attached electrodes that recorded electroencephalogram readings of Skylab astronauts was adapted to provide greatly simplified methods for obtaining EEG information that determines dysfunctions in the human nervous system, especially among disturbed children; (3) a device for measuring astronauts' respiration was used to observe and study epileptic seizures; (4) a radiographic image processing technique for improving the quality of space photographs was modified to aid in studies of blood circulation through the heart, and to speed the diagnosis of coronary disease.

When Brown became systems engineering research manager, leadership of the BATeam fell to Wooten, who held the position for seven years. More recently, since 1980, BAT and TATeam efforts have been headed by Doris J. Rouse, director of RTI's Center for Technology Applications.

Through the transition from BAT to TAT she says that the transfer of space research to earthly applications still involves a commitment to biomedical and rehabilitation engineering, but also that it has expanded to encompass other high technology enterprises such as automation, telerobotics, materials and market research, and industrial processes.

A handful of recent TATeam solutions: (1) The continuous casting of long slabs of steel has caused problems for American manufacturers because compressing the steel cracks the rollers that are used in the process. Coating the rollers with an alloy developed for rocket nose cones extends the life of process surfaces in steel production. (2) Space vehicle launch control systems have been adapted to monitor the automated operations of textile manufacturers and electric utilities. (3) The control mechanism of NASA's lunar rover was the basis for a development that allows physically handicapped persons to drive what's called a Unistik vehicle equipped with a device that controls direction, speed, gear shift, and braking. (4) Liquid-cooled garments adapted from astronauts' space suits aid people who are born without sweat glands to keep their body temperature below dangerous levels.

Sometimes a technology transfer can involve what amounts to a matter of public policy, going beyond the usual engineering response to a specific need in medicine or industry.

RTI's wandering-detection device is a perfect example, using technology transfer to help meet safety and health goals, social goals, and the concerns of five federal agencies. It also illustrates the care with which transfer candidates are selected, and the TATeam's interdisciplinary approach.

Wandering is defined as movement by a memory-impaired person that puts that person in danger. Wandering occurs within and near homes and apartments, and in institutional settings. It affects tens of thousands of Alzheimer's disease patients and others who suffer memory loss, threatening them with the risk of accident and injury. As for wanderers' families, they can be afflicted by exhaustion, anxiety, and restricted movement. Expense, too, for professional care in the home can be very costly. So can nursing homes, often with the added cost of a wrenching emotional experience.

Realizing the threats that various forms and degrees of memory loss pose to the elderly, and seeking means to postpone or prevent confinement in an institution, five agencies acting together in May of 1985 commissioned RTI's TATeam to devise new measures and techniques that would address this aspect of older people's health and social needs. The five, including NASA, are the Administration on Aging, Veterans Administration, National Institute on Aging, and National Institute on Handicapped Research.

RTI convened an advisory panel that narrowed the target population to those who would benefit most, that is, to those with clinically mild to moderate cognitive impairments. The panel selected this group because of the large number of people in it, because many of them live at home but are nearing institutionalization, and because their needs are largely unmet by assist devices.

The panel next identified three specific memory-related problems affecting this population: medication dispensing and dosage compliance, incontinence, and wandering. The sponsoring agencies decided to tackle wandering.

To aid in the investigation of the prevalence and consequences of wandering, project leader Rouse, whose Ph.D. is in physiology and pharmacology, reached into RTI's Center for Policy Studies for the support of Janet D. Griffith, who holds a doctorate in social relations. Among wandering's positive consequences for the wanderer, they concluded, are the opportunities for stimulation, exercise and sociability, maintenance of a feeling of independence and self-worth, and a sense of continuity with earlier life roles, no matter how faint or fleeting that sense might be. Potential negative consequences for the wanderer include physical harm from injury or exposure, panic at being lost and, if kept under restraint, the loss of freedom to move about.

Negative consequences for family members were a major consideration. They included fear for the wanderer's safety, and physical and mental tolls from the need for constant vigilance. The researchers learned that wandering is what many caregivers cite as their main reason for putting an elderly person into a nursing home.

They also found a number of warning-detection devices on the market, but none of them applicable for home use. Finding such a device that served such a purpose became the sponsoring agencies' first priority. Rouse, Griffith, and others conceptualized the solution as a unit, perhaps the size of a wristwatch, that would be worn by the wanderer and would transmit a signal to the caregiver's unit. At a prearranged distance, the weakening signal would set off alarms in both units, alerting the wanderer (assuming cognitive awareness) and warning the caregiver that the former was about to stray beyond safe limits.

A means to meet the needs was defined, but where to find it? Technology utilization officers at each of NASA's nine centers went to work to sift out appropriate possibilities. The most promising came from the Johnson Space Center in Texas. It was a NASA technology for monitoring spacecraft as they carry out docking maneuvers and, more pertinent to the issue at hand, that tracks astronauts as they perform extravehicular activities in space.

Private sector involvement, prototype device design, and product feasibility and marketing evaluations followed. Sometime in 1990, five years after beginning to address the wanderer's problem, NASA and RTI hope a device will be in clinical testing, the last stage before a product becomes commercially available.

Assessment

It was the biggest and most innovative and very likely the most significant effort of its kind, and for nearly 15 years the National Assessment of Educational Progress (NAEP) devoured the time and energies of a major segment of RTI's sampling statisticians and survey specialists, of several dozen regional and district supervisors around the country, and of up to 500 and more temporary field personnel who might be needed at any given time.

Beginning in February 1969 and extending into 1983, when another contractor took over, RTI was responsible for conducting and administering NAEP, the first comprehensive attempt to obtain census-like data about the knowledge, skills, and attitudes of America's young people, and to measure changes in these attributes over time.

Actually, RTI's association began in 1966, not 1969, and assessment's name then wasn't NAEP but ECAPE. This Exploratory Committee on Assessing the Progress of Education was already being financed by the Carnegie Corporation and Ford Foundation when Gertrude Cox and Dan

Horvitz were asked to meet with the committee to talk about some of the sampling and survey methodology considerations that would have to be taken into account in launching ECAPE's rather ambitious study. Rather ambitious? In magnitude, complexity, and purpose, NAEP has been unique among educational surveys.

Its aim has been to determine if the nation's schoolchildren are learning as much as educators expect them to, if they are making educational progress. Assessment results have been major news from the start in both general and professional media, especially, as in 1989, when they can report items such as disappointing functional illiteracy rates or students' widespread inability to give correct answers to simple geography questions. Positive results occur, too, however, and both kinds are invaluable as a statistically reliable report card to guide policymakers, planners, administrators, teachers, teachers' teachers, and parents.

NAEP encountered some initial resistance from defenders of local school system autonomy who feared assessment as a wedge that might ultimately lead to national grading standards and a mandated curriculum, but eventually it was supported by teacher, administrator, school board, and government organizations, and more than 3,000 of their representatives participated in ECAPE's planning and preparations.

As statisticians concerned with groups of people and what they think and do, Cox and Horvitz were intrigued by the committee's concepts and intentions. They were impressed but not intimidated by the statistical and survey research hurdles that clearly lay ahead.

The basic concept: By periodically measuring the knowledge, skills, and attitudes of young people in each of four age groups, find out if they are learning as much as educators think they should be learning, if educational quality is improving or declining.

The primary intention: To make this measurement, at three- to five-year intervals continuously repeat the administration of written, oral, and demonstration exercises in various subjects to a very large national sample of 9-year-olds, 13-year-olds, 17-year-olds, and adults age 26 to 35. With the first year's assessment results in any subject as a benchmark, analysts can use data from subsequent cycles to gauge any growth or decline in overall student achievement.

Seeking information from age groups, rather than from more easily identifiable grade levels, was one of NAEP's unique features and one of RTI's toughest problems. There's general grade-level uniformity for each age group but, even so, students in any of the first three age groups could often be found in two and sometimes three grades, a range that gave RTI statistical scientists something more than the usual difficulties in selecting representative random samples of individuals. A further complication was that special sampling frames had to be constructed for 17-year-olds who had already graduated or dropped out, and who might be hard to locate. They and the 26-35 age group completed their exercises at home, while students did theirs during school hours.

By the time field operations began in 1969, RTI statistical studies had validated NAEP's novel approaches to data collection, the project was being funded through the National Assessment office by the National Center for Educational Statistics, and Al Finkner's Statistics Research Division was geared up to carry out what was then the Institute's biggest project by far in terms of most recruiting, most interviewing, most paperwork, most dollars, most data, and most frequent use of the word "unprecedented." NAEP's initial project leader was William C. Eckerman, who was RTI's first Ph.D. social psychologist and had joined the staff in 1967 after six years with the University of Michigan's Survey Research Center. James R. Chromy was head of sampling and design, and would succeed Eckerman as project leader. Survey operations in the field, including interviewer training and exercise administration, were headed by William K. Grogan.

Surveying students by age rather than grade level was only one of NAEP's departures from educational evaluation norms.* Perhaps the most important was that assessment exercises were just that, exercises not tests. There was no individual grading of responses to the exercise questions. There were right answers and wrong answers, but they weren't rewarded or penalized. Similarly, there was no individual ranking of students, or schools, or districts, or states, nothing competitive. The idea was not to rank and compare—many testing instruments are available for those purposes—but to obtain information that describes how accurately the average of all students responded to each question. (Interviewer observation was the basis for judging student performance on discussion and demonstration exercises. Examples: describe functions of the legislative branch of government; balance weights on a pair of scales.)

Ten subjects for assessment had been recommended by the committee and its advisers. These were science, citizenship, writing, reading, literature, music, social studies, mathematics, occupational development, and art. All were covered at least once, for all age groups, during the first six years of assessment. They and other topics added later were, and continue to be, covered in subsequent cycles.

* And one that has been discontinued, since RTI's participation ended, in favor of the less rigorous drawing of samples from the 4th, 8th, and 12th grades.

During RTI's first ten years of responsibility, NAEP exercises were administered to about one million persons, an average annual sample of some 100,000. Any survey even approaching that magnitude was remarkable then and is unusual now.

An Organizational Change

Additions to and changes within RTI's research organization are commonplace. Imperative, too, for in this most dynamic of businesses new ideas and new opportunities continually arise; new knowledge and new technologies enhance researchers' resources; new markets are identified and new problems emerge; and the corporate organism must adjust to accommodate them all.

RTI's adjustments in the early years were pretty much along disciplinary lines, and took the form of adding new laboratories and divisions in response to favorable circumstance and inviting prospect. Hence the eight-unit research grouping that existed in the spring of 1964 with creation of the Geophysics Laboratory. Other adjustments were name changes that reflected marketing and/or research capability priorities. "Isotopes development" became "measurements and controls" in April 1961, for example, "economics" was added to "operations research" in August 1964 and, perhaps most significantly in terms of both market and resources, in November 1966 the Natural Products Laboratory became the Chemistry and Life Sciences Laboratory.

Windfalls like the Dreyfus Foundation grant and the Atomic Energy Commission assignment can be hoped for, but hardly counted upon. Occasionally, reputation alone is sufficient to bring a research assignment. During the sixties and seventies and eighties, however, essentially all the new directions taken by RTI resulted from what most businesses know as program development. This is the process of investing relatively patient money to hire and support new staff to take research initiatives in new fields with the expectation that within a reasonable time prospective clients will have been cultivated, proposals will have been accepted, and contract revenue will be yielding a satisfactory return on investment.

Except for isotopes and polymers, and statistics to a small degree, this kind of program development investment launched all of RTI's early research units.

The first new direction taken by RTI that was also an adjustment more substantial than a name change occurred in August 1967. It was a consequence of that summer's decision to try to double the Institute's size in five years time. The intention was to achieve this growth by expanding the scope of RTI research, an expansion for which staff resources were readily apparent in the larger divisions. Resources were not so apparent in the four smaller laboratories. These were measurements and controls under Orcutt, solid state under Burger, geophysics under Worth, and radiation systems under Charles L. (Les) Britt, acting director since P. Gene Smith's resignation.

Despite fine leadership, staff, and research record, the business prospects for these laboratories were confined to relatively narrow and very competitive markets. Lacking the critical mass of research opportunities on which the larger units (statistics, ORE, chemistry) were able to base new departures and advanced programs, their growth opportunities were limited by size and fragmentation. In combination, the four had fewer than 50 of RTI's approximately 300 staff members, and 15 active projects with an aggregate annual funding of about three-quarters of a million dollars. (RTI's total revenue for the year, 1967, was $4.7 million; five years later it had indeed more than doubled to $9.9 million.)

On August 24 Herbert announced that staff and programs of the four laboratories were being combined into a single Engineering and Environmental Sciences Division (EESD). "If we are to be a vital organization in the 1970s, contributing significantly through our research accomplishments, the engineering sciences and the study of man's physical environment must represent an important segment of [our] activity," he wrote. Also, "The flexibility resulting from this . . . change will enable us to guide our planning decisions towards those national and regional research needs in which our professional staff has special competence."

In charge of filling up an EESD organization chart that was empty except for themselves were division director Bob Burger and deputy director Jim Pearson, an electrical engineering graduate of N.C. State who had been with a Florida electronics firm for three years before joining RTI in the fall of 1961. He transferred to engineering and environmental sciences from the Office of Research Contracts, which once more was temporarily added to Bill Perkins' already full plate of responsibilities.

Burger and Pearson devised an initial operating plan that in all respects but one was jim-dandy: Jim Brown headed systems and instrumentation, Jim Smith headed sensor development, Jim Worth headed environmental sciences, and Jim Wortman headed advanced studies, a catchall for fundamental research covering the complete spectrum of the division's scientific activities. Larry Monteith headed semiconductor materials and devices.

By early summer of 1968 Pearson had left RTI and Burger and Worth, by now associate EESD director, put a slightly different but more cohesive set-up into effect. Wortman was manager of engineering physics, Smith of environmental sciences, and Brown of systems engineering. (Monteith had joined the electrical engineering faculty at N.C. State, where he would become engineering dean and chancellor.) This divisional arrangement held until September 1971 and a major restructuring of RTI research operations.

The emergence of "environmental sciences," both as the division's second name and as a rapidly growing part of RTI research, was no accident. For one thing, pollution abatement and health effects were increasingly matters of national concern, debate, and funding. For another, Chet Clark pressed hard to engage these concerns with RTI's skills in meteorology, sensors, measurement techniques, and instrumentation systems. When he arrived at RTI in August 1965, America's basic clean air and environmental protection legislation was more than four years in the future, but it wasn't long before "he began pushing us to get involved, to go to Cincinnati." The words are from Jim Worth, who in 1971 was elected vice president of RTI's environmental sciences (now the first name) and engineering group.

Cincinnati's attraction was the National Center for Air Pollution Control. Until the EPA was created in 1970 (by merger of 15 federal agencies and programs), and its massive Environmental Research Center completed in the Research Triangle Park the following year, Cincinnati was the largest scientific center for air pollution research and control technology. Worth and others did go to Cincinnati and also to pollution control offices in Washington. The associations they formed at both locations served RTI well when the EPA technical center for air pollution control moved to North Carolina. (Among those who made the trip to Cincinnati in 1966 was Cliff Decker, who stayed for two years. A graduate student of Ripperton's at UNC, Decker worked a year at RTI, then spent two as a Public Health Service officer in Cincinnati, where he was chief of source gas analysis. He returned to RTI and since 1983 has been director of the Center for Environmental Measurements.)

With its revved-up potential for growth, formation of the Engineering and Environmental Sciences Division was easily the most significant management move of the late sixties. Other changes of interest were also being put into place as the decade drew to a close. For example, anticipating the need to get set with a senior administrative structure for handling the staff and program expansions that would follow the 1971 move from Bacon Street to the RTPark, chemistry and life sciences director Wall named Ivy Carroll, Ed Cook, and Keith Palmer as group leaders.

Bud Parsons resigned from operations research and economics in February 1969 and was replaced by Ralph Ely as acting director. Ely's RTI assignments had by then included isotopes development, the Office of Industry Services (see Chapter 13), and the environmental health sciences panel. Other posts were in his future. He left intact the organization of Bryan, Ed Hill, and McMullan as group leaders, and he and Clark established within the division an Office of State and Regional Planning, which is also described in Chapter 13. Ely was succeeded in October by Jay T. Wakeley, an N.C. State Ph.D. in experimental statistics who had spent 15 years in California with the Rand Corporation, North American Aviation, and the General Research Corporation.

In statistics, Finkner's organization since mid-1968 had included Horvitz as deputy director, Sweeny at the head of applied statistics and special projects, Chromy, head of sampling, Grogan of survey operations, A. Carl Nelson, Jr., of systems statistics, and Eckerman of social statistics. In the fall of 1969, Finkner and Horvitz brought in Quentin S. Lindsey as manager of population planning and population statistics. His Ph.D. in economics was from Harvard and his experience included seven years on N.C. State's faculty, seven in Burma and Nepal as a Ford Foundation adviser, and one at UNC's Carolina Population Center.

Research on societal problems was nothing new to the Statistics Research Division. Nevertheless, departmental designations for social sciences and for population studies were substantive events in RTI's development and its opportunities for service in the national interest.

13. Postscripts to the Sixties

North Carolina Industry

More than anyone else, Herbert has been mindful of RTI's obligations to the state that gave it birth. This awareness complements, and by no means conflicts with, his understanding that the Institute's success and growth necessarily issue from the work that a gifted and multidisciplinary staff performs for a varied national and international clientele. The sense of obligation is consistent with the circumstances of RTI's establishment, for concept, form, and funding make it unique to North Carolina.

Going into the mid-sixties, RTI's basic objectives were being achieved. The Institute was self-supporting, stable, growing. Its reputation for high-quality research was notable, and widening. Its staff was respected by federal agencies and major corporations, precisely the clientele that was necessary to success.

But, as Herbert said at the November 5, 1969, annual board meeting, "There was, however, one big 'But.' But we must do more than simply reside in the state and region that created us; we must find ways, without changing our principal direction, to apply some of the capabilities assembled and developed at RTI to the opportunities and problems of industry and government in our area."

The intellectual priority that Herbert gave to serving North Carolina industry did not translate into precipitate action. He knew well enough that the senior staff's primary attention would always center on national themes and problems, whether of government or of industry. Success in cultivating such national involvement was the means by which RTI could create the resources that would enable it to address regional concerns. There was no rush.

A substantial resource directed to regional needs almost from RTI's start was the Isotopes Development Laboratory. During the first two years of the Atomic Energy Commission contract, RTI was required to take the lead in identifying radioisotope methods that could help improve regional industry's processes and products, and then work with individual companies to apply those methods. Laboratory director Ralph Ely made contacts throughout the state, and was welcomed by large and small firms alike. After all, his and RTI's services were free, paid for by the AEC. A company's costs, if any, would come with investment in the measurement gauges, radiotracing instruments, or other process controls that had been recommended to increase efficiency.

There was no rush, but the going on several technical marketing fronts was disappointingly slow. When RTI's obligation to concentrate on industrial applications of radioisotopes ended after two years, Ely found an expanding client base within the AEC and other agencies. As for regional industry, the firms he had previously worked with had little or nothing in their backgrounds that would lead them to pay for research except through membership in their industry associations.

And there were other disappointments. A symposium at RTI to discuss operations research applications to the production, distribution, and planning processes of the textiles industry drew good attendance, but generated no contract opportunities. The trustees of the Cotton Producers Institute spent a day at RTI for demonstrations and presentations, but none of the individual companies represented became a client. The N.C. Board of Science and Technology paid for an RTI engineering and marketing analysis of methods for increasing the use of prefabricated clay products in construction, and while RTI's ideas received favorable comment within the brick and tile industry, further research funds weren't forthcoming.

Structured approaches to aiding North Carolina businesses obviously weren't working, so Herbert tried a new tack. Early in 1965 Ely was given a new assignment as head of an RTI Office of Industry Services. He would be a one-man referral service, a clearinghouse or idea broker for North Carolina businessmen and manufacturers who encountered technical difficulties they didn't have the resources to solve.

The new office was a made-to-order mechanism for giving direct, pragmatic assistance to North Carolina companies without diluting the energies needed for RTI's major research programs. It was eminently practical, and it was successful. When a problem came to Ely he could sometimes suggest a solution out of his own experience. More often, however, he went to an RTI specialist for advice, or referred the inquiry to a university faculty member, to a commercial testing laboratory, or to a private consulting firm. Herbert made it clear that the success of the effort would not be measured by research contracts obtained but, rather, by service provided to N.C. companies. Ely's time was free. When another RTI professional spent more than a day or two on a problem, a nominal charge was sometimes made. During its four-year existence the Office of Industry Services lived up to its name; records weren't kept, but dozens and dozens of problems were received, examined, and solved.

The informal, one-man-gang approach worked, even while the Institute continued to find it difficult "to apply [its] capabilities . . . to the problems of industry . . . in our area."

A primary obstacle was cited by Herbert in a November 1972 talk at the NCSU Pulp and Paper Foundation's annual board meeting. He referenced a National Science Foundation finding that the group of industries with the lowest annual research investment, less than 1.0 percent of their sales dollars, included: textiles and apparel; lumber, wood products, and furniture; and paper and allied products—the very industries that traditionally sustained North Carolina's labor-intensive economy and its low per capita income ranking. The state's other major nonfarm industry, tobacco products, had a better research-as-a-percent-of-sales ratio, but RTI's work for cigarette companies has been limited to fewer than a dozen small projects.

As far as RTI has been concerned, the research of most value to North Carolina textile companies has been under contracts sponsored by industry-wide organizations. The National Cotton Council, Cotton Incorporated, and the American Textile Manufacturers Institute were at one time frequent RTI clients for research in chemistry, physics, and statistical analysis. RTI's volume of work for companies and associations in the furniture and paper categories has been even less than for tobacco interests.

By the time Herbert made his 1972 talk, the Research Triangle idea had become a force which even the most optimistic had not, and could not have, anticipated. Fueled by the Triangle universities and North Carolina's community colleges and technical institutes, and with RTI as its earliest manifestation, a whole new dimension was being built into the state's economy. Growth in the Research Triangle Park and the three-county Research Triangle area had the greatest visibility, but high-tech enterprise was on the rise in other parts of the state, too.

The increasing technological sophistication of the state's industry signaled an increase in the potential for RTI's scientific and engineering talents to serve private sector markets. Research revenue from this North Carolina market has been modest, but RTI/industry ties are solid, and they underscore RTI's role as a provider of specialty research services for companies in the state.

Herbert has emphasized RTI's private sector involvement by pointing to the large number of contracts involved rather than to the quantity of revenue dollars generated. During 1989, one-third of RTI's active projects were for commercial clients. These 200 projects were for more than 120 companies, 34 of them North Carolina firms, in fields as diverse as pharmaceutical compounds, manufacturing productivity, electric utility rates, clean room technology, and computer-aided software engineering.

State of North Carolina

Governor Robert W. Scott talking in November 1971: "I wish all the people who are after my job could have heard this for advance notice about some of the problems they'd face."

What he referred to were projections of North Carolina population, employment, personal income, and tax revenue trends through the decade of the 1970s prepared by RTI's Office of State and Regional Planning (OSRP) and presented to Scott and other officials at a seminar in the Camille Dreyfus auditorium.

He also said that for lack of information three years earlier, during his own election campaign,* he had not been able to speak as knowledgeably as he wished about state finances and budget expectations. But now he could offer his successor a helping hand, and did so by inviting all of 1972's candidates for governor and lieutenant governor to Raleigh for a March 6 briefing at which OSRP deputy head Al Cruze reviewed and highlighted results of the analyses. All 16 candidates were represented, ten in person, six by senior aides.

Scott's unusual political gesture was a highlight in itself, but didn't arise from RTI's first research for state government. The first project, completed in March 1965, was a survey of fuel consumption by gasoline-powered boats. Its findings, along with those of a follow-on four years later, became the basis for state gas tax allocations to the Wildlife Resources Commission. The next two state projects dealt with low-cost housing and with sampling procedures for surveying child day-care facilities. Over the years, research for the State of North Carolina has covered nursing home services, fuel conservation, environmental measurements, alcoholism, bicycle safety, and chemical problems associated with drug abuse and with blood analysis.

By far the greatest part of research for the state, however, has been in the fields of economic planning and human and natural resource development, and its greatest concentration was between 1965 and 1976, the two dates marking James A. Street's arrival at RTI and his departure to open the Institute's ill-fated office in Charlotte.

Regional economics and area development research were Herbert priorities for RTI, and during his years at Stanford Research Institute he had seen how successful they could be, but the few RTI economists who were at all interested had a basically academic orientation, little or no hands-on experience, and slight inclination to mix into the rough and tumble of state

* Prior to James B. Hunt's occupancy of the executive mansion, North Carolina's constitution prohibited the state's governor from serving consecutive terms.

bureaucratic and legislative affairs. Herbert found what he was looking for when Street, who was born for the role, showed up in September 1965. (Cruze joined RTI at the same time, but he and Street didn't become a team until several years later.) Street had degrees in agricultural economics from the University of Kentucky and a background of research on federal redevelopment programs in Appalachia, tobacco marketing, 20-year industry trends and resource use projections in the Ohio River Valley, and a year abroad analyzing the demand for soybean products in the European Economic Community.

Assigned to vice president Chet Clark's office to establish an RTI regional research identity, Street spent most of his time for two years on loan to the State Planning Task Force that Governor Dan K. Moore had recently created to look around the corners of North Carolina's economic future. It was an ideal means for him to become familiar with the issues—the state's economic assets, problems, requirements, and opportunities—and with the people responsible for dealing with them—appointed and elected officials, career employees, consultants. It also gave him a chance to become almost as familiar as any state planner with the programs of various federal agencies as they pertained to North Carolina, and with those of multistate bodies such as the Coastal Plains Regional Commission and the Appalachian Regional Commission, both of which became RTI research clients.

Where Governor Moore had accepted the Institute as a participant in North Carolina's preparation for change, Governor Scott engaged it as a full partner in the process. Dozens of projects were undertaken in cooperation with state agencies: an analysis of outdoor recreation resources; enlarged and improved state parks and state forests; long-range plans for the community college system; trends in manpower utilization and labor productivity; a major management information and evaluation role in the state's new highway safety program.

By the time the Office of State and Regional Planning was upgraded, in April 1973, to Center for Development and Resource Planning, the limitations of the earlier name had been stretched through planning and economic development contracts with neighboring and nearby states, and with independent, federally-funded agencies.

For the Coastal Plains Regional Commission, for example, there was a summary of planning and economics research on water, power, and fuel resources covering 159 counties in the Carolinas and Georgia. With funding from the Federal Aviation Administration, RTI took on a 22-month assignment to make a 20-year forecast of the needs for runways, freight operations, terminal space, surface transportation, and other services at the different classes of airports in North Carolina. America's reliance on coal as a primary energy source increased dramatically in the 1970s and, in research for the Appalachian Regional Commission, RTI and N.C. State University found that the coal-producing areas of the Appalachian states were woefully short of funds (perhaps $5 billion in 1977 dollars) for keeping coal-haul roads and bridges in safe condition.

Strictly at home, meanwhile, millions of North Carolinians' convenience and comfort were served by changes in the state's vehicle registration system that followed a wide-ranging RTI analysis of N.C. Department of Motor Vehicles operations. Thanks to P. Nileen Hunt, Bob Thornton, and other analysts, 1975 was the last year that motor vehicle owners had to endure the annual agony of standing in long, and often cold, lines to purchase new license plates. Renewal procedures under which expiration dates occur on a staggered basis throughout the year went into effect in 1976. Until then, all license tags had expired on December 31, with new plates required for display by February 15. RTI recommendations also led to the adoption of renewal stickers, rather than new plates every year, and to their distribution by mail rather than by personal pick-up.

A Digression

Herbert said there wasn't a chance in the world, but even so a proposal from Street's center won the competition for a U.S. Treasury Department contract to make a 15-year forecast of the nation's coinage system requirements. The research was to consider changes in coin materials, production technology, distribution methods, and denominations (legislation had been introduced in Congress to authorize the minting of 2-cent and 12½-cent coins.) In what a treasury official called "a darn good study," RTI's 1976 report covered all these topics in detail. However, no one except the Bureau of the Mint and its suppliers noticed the substantial economies that the report promised, or anything else about the study except its recommendations to eliminate the penny and to mint a new and more convenient dollar coin to replace the unpopular Kennedy half-dollars and Eisenhower dollars that were then circulating, or, rather, not circulating.

Getting rid of the penny was an idea that found no popular favor whatever, but the prospect of a handier dollar had considerable appeal. The opinions of mint officials and of vending machine manufacturers and users were combined with RTI survey research results to indicate a consensus on the desired size, shape, and color of the coin: Its looks and feel should be distinctive. (In case any of this sounds familiar, the same arguments surfaced in support of 1990 legislative proposals to abolish the penny and mint a new "Columbus" dollar.) Sadly, after the politicians and special interests had their way, what emerged into public view on July 2, 1979, was a silver coin whose appearance, far from being distinctive, is virtually indistinguishable from the George Washington 25-cent piece. The Susan B. Anthony dollar was a total flop, the public would have nothing to do with it, and this digression is necessary because too many people who didn't pay attention retain the mistaken impression that RTI recommended the coin's design.

The Charlotte Office

Dean Colvard (see Chapter 1) was chancellor of the University of North Carolina at Charlotte in March 1975 when he and Herbert told a news conference that RTI and the university would work together to establish a permanent RTI branch in Charlotte. The city's political and business communities were pleased by the announcement, UNCC's Institute for Urban Studies and Community Services was enthusiastic, and Jim Street received a warm welcome when he came to town as branch director in July of the following year.

Herbert and Street anticipated that RTI's 11 successful years in regional economics, state planning, and area development would lead to related research activities for city and county governments and businesses not only in Charlotte and Mecklenburg County, but also in other states and regions. Despite high hopes and strenuous efforts, it didn't work out. Sufficient business just wasn't there, and home-based staff, with their own commitments and priorities, showed little enthusiasm for opportunities developed by the staff in Charlotte. Street phased out operations there and returned to RTI in July 1978.

The Governors

Actions during the terms of Governor Luther Hodges (1954-60) and Governor Terry Sanford (1961-64) were crucial to RTI's development, and Governors Dan Moore (1965-1968) and James E. Holshouser, Jr., (1973-76) were supportive, though less directly involved.

The Governor/RTI relationship came to its fullest flower during Bob Scott's years in office, 1969 through 1972. There's little question that RTI was Scott's favorite not-for-profit research institute. A few examples of projects initiated during his administration have been given, though what he liked and admired most were the capabilities for long-range planning, economic forecasting, and data management. If the results of RTI research indicated an executive action, he almost always took it, and when they didn't he paid attention anyway.

Scott got personal about it, too. He didn't have to be in attendance at RTI annual and semiannual meetings, but he usually was. He didn't have to be present at research review and decisionmaking sessions between senior state officers and RTI staff, but he often was. He didn't have to represent the U.S. Department of Commerce by personally presenting RTI's Jim Smith with an award for his role as chief scientific coordinator for RTI and other North Carolina institutions that took part in an experimental meteorology research voyage through the Caribbean (see Chapter 12), but he did.

And he certainly didn't have to think of expressing himself toward RTI by inviting a group of staff, board members, and spouses for a Christmas season evening at the Governor's Mansion, but he did think of it. In accepting the invitation, Herbert wrote that it was "about the finest tribute that could be paid to our staff," and in his letter of thanks following the event he wrote that "the warmth which you and Mrs. Scott gave to the occasion left all of us with the feeling of friends who had been invited into your home for the evening."

Scott was succeeded by Holshouser, whose administration also called upon RTI's resources, and Holshouser by James B. Hunt, Jr., (1977-84). As Scott had, Hunt often seemed to regard RTI as an arm of his own office, but with a twist. The first arm he twisted belonged to Jimmie Wortman, who was by then director of RTI's Energy and Environmental Research Division. For most of Hunt's first term Wortman was chairman of the Governor's Task Force on Energy, giving it virtually full time for the first six months. Wortman was also Hunt's appointee as chairman of the N.C. Alternative Energy Corporation and as N.C. representative on the Southern Interstate Nuclear Board (the technical and scientific energy arm of the Southern Governors Conference). Full time or part time, Wortman's time was all donated by RTI. Scott hadn't thought of this wrinkle, but Hunt worked it to perfection, and his next target was Herbert. Twice.

One of Hunt's truly great initiatives for North Carolina was creation of the nation's first residential public high school, a state-supported boarding school, for youngsters gifted in the sciences and mathematics. He named Herbert as planning committee chairman in 1978. After the plans became reality, Herbert served for two years as vice chairman of the board of the N.C. School of Science and Mathematics, located in Durham.

Pretty soon Triangle university and RTI achievements were among the ingredients that again gave Hunt an idea for another national first, the first state-supported center devoted to microelectronics research, a scientific magnet for attracting high-tech R&D and manufacturing dollars to the state. In 1980 Herbert became planning committee chairman for this, too, and continued on for a total of eight years as board chairman of the Microelectronics Center of North Carolina. Located in the Research Triangle Park, MCNC is a consortium whose participating institutions are NCSU, Duke, UNC-Chapel Hill, North Carolina A&T State University in Greensboro, UNC-Charlotte, and RTI.

With 1989 assets of nearly $58 million, MCNC is a big operation for a state like North Carolina, and a unique operation for any state. Getting it all organized, coordinated, explained (again and again), lobbied, funded, staffed, and operating was such a time-consuming proposition that Herbert felt obliged to counter published news accounts by assuring RTI's staff that he had not taken, and would not take, a leave of absence. It was gratifying to the individuals and the Institute to enjoy so much of the governor's confidence and attention, but if Hunt had "borrowed" Wortman and Herbert for the two other volunteer posts, he essentially kidnapped Herbert for MCNC.

Governor Hunt's regard for RTI continued after his term ended in 1985, and even extended to an Institute economic feasibility study for a group with which the former governor was associated. While they were in office, Hunt and his predecessors—Holshouser, Scott, Moore, and back through Sanford and Hodges—took a personal interest in RTI activities, and they retained their interest after leaving office.

Institute research for North Carolina, and for other states as well, has continued to involve many topics and many disciplines. Nearly all of the research has had positive outcomes, none more pleasurable to report than a 1971 project whose forecasts on potential economic return were essential to the N.C. General Assembly's appropriation of funds to build a state zoo. It's located on 1,445 acres at Purgatory Mountain in Asheboro, near the center of the state.

Quality of Life

The "war on poverty" bill that became law on August 20, 1964, created an Office of Economic Opportunity (OEO) in the Executive Office of the President. It offered federal funding for such Great Society programs as Job Corps training for school dropouts, Head Start for disadvantaged preschoolers, Upward Bound for disadvantaged high school students, the Neighborhood Youth Corps, Aid to Families with Dependent Children, and food stamps.

All were to benefit from RTI's resources in survey research and the social sciences, beginning with a project that started in September 1965 for the OEO-supported North Carolina Fund.

Since then, RTI data gathering and evaluation projects have aided additional federal agencies (Departments of Agriculture, Defense, Health and Human Services, Labor) that have been responsible for other major social programs. (The OEO itself was disbanded in 1975.) An Institute analysis of the WIC nutrition programs was a national news topic as recently as January 1990, for example.

WIC, the Special Supplemental Food Program for Women, Infants and Children, began in 1972 and is overseen by the U.S. Department of Agriculture (USDA). Administered at the local level, WIC enrolls low-income pregnant women, breast-feeding mothers, infants, and preschool children, offering food supplements, nutrition education, and health care counseling. RTI was in on WIC almost, but not quite, from the word go. Congress stipulated that before the program was implemented on a national scale, some twenty local demonstration projects were to be set up around the country and their effectiveness gauged by medical examinations that would establish whether there were measurable improvements in the overall health of participants. By the end of 1973 UNC-Chapel Hill had obtained the medical evaluation award and RTI became statistical coordinator for the collection, processing, and analysis of clinical data and associated personal information on about 30,000 children and 15,000 women, a major data coordinating and reporting task. Ken Poole of statistical methodology headed RTI's 21-month effort. The UNC/RTI results confirmed that the local projects' goals were being met.

Beginning ten years later, in 1982, RTI and the New York State Research Foundation for Mental Health were embarked upon the first national evaluation of WIC, with Horvitz as project director and economist Sally S. Johnson as manager and coordinator of the team of survey specialists and statistical and social scientists. The range of information to be sought was so great that the researchers decided against a single, comprehensive survey. Instead, they designed four separate but interrelated studies and conducted them concurrently. At the end of 1985, some of the findings in their five-volume report dealt with: infants' birthweight, length, head circumference; mothers' education, prenatal care, weight and subcutaneous fat changes, smoking habits, alcohol consumption; preschoolers' intake of iron and vitamins, their height and weight, memory and vocabulary, immunization history; households' nutritional habits, food expenditures, meals away from home, health care needs. The evaluation (which was not immediately released in its entirety by the USDA to Congress) showed clearly that WIC improves mothers' health, reduces infant mortality, and helps to give newborns and young children a healthy start in life.

An "error-prone profile" is the management control by which RTI helped the State of North Carolina avoid a $3.5 million penalty that the USDA threatened to levy in 1982 because the state had distributed over $13 million worth of food stamps in error, an amount exceeding the permissible national standard. The penalty was waived when the USDA accepted the state's plan, which included the error-prone profile, for reducing the number of food stamp coupons issued in error. Through methods analogous to the way the Internal Revenue Service decides which income tax returns are the best candidates for audit, RTI policy analysts found two characteristics common to those households for which sizeable errors in food stamp allotments were likely to occur. These were that almost one-fourth of households that had both five or more persons and some earned income also had errors of more than $50 in their food stamp allotments. (Only 2 percent of one-person households were likely to have a food stamp error.) Although only one-tenth of errors involved $50 or more, they accounted for more than two-thirds of the total amount misspent. Instead of treating all food stamp applications and verifications alike, RTI recommended that county food stamp agencies focus their examiners' energies on larger households and those reporting some earned income. Successful testing of the profile method led to its adoption not only in North Carolina, but also in several other states.

Food stamps, WIC, Head Start, Upward Bound, and similar projects fall under a general heading of "quality of life" research. The term first appeared in the official RTI record when Finkner described some of its potentials at an Executive Committee meeting in February 1965. It gained currency at about the same time, at least in the Statistics Research Division, with preparations for the North Carolina Fund project. To be dwarfed soon enough by monumental health, educational, and environmental surveys, the N.C. Fund survey was RTI's biggest until then, big enough to be "massive by any standard except that of the U.S. Bureau of the Census," as Horvitz put it at the time.

The N.C. Fund supported local action programs in 11 communities around the state. Their aim was to improve the economic well-being of low income families by creating new educational and employment opportunities. The success of the projects couldn't be confirmed, however, until before-and-after measurements were made. RTI's survey fixed the "before" benchmarks. By adapting RTI's procedures, the Fund expected to make the follow-up in about three years. How massive was the first phase? Long before the days when computer-assisted data gathering became routine for RTI survey research, the Institute's 150 interviewers visited 12,500 North Carolina households, spending about an hour at each to ask more than 400 questions. They recorded nearly 5.5 million answers.

The increasing emphasis on quality of life research at RTI coincided with rising public concerns over environmental, health, education, and welfare issues. In the span of just a few years the shift in RTI activity was dramatic. In 1966, research in health, education, population, environment, and transportation accounted for 21 percent of the Institute's revenue, the balance coming from contracts for research in civil defense, electronics, polymers, and system reliability. Just three years later, in 1969, those quality of life categories had risen to represent 65 percent of total research revenue. And just three years after that the figure was 80 percent.

Specific examples of this redirection illustrate the changes better than numbers do. Drug metabolism studies, with their implications for new and improved contraceptive compounds, had come to constitute the largest single program in chemistry and life sciences.* Systems engineers who had analyzed altimeter radars for lunar landing modules were now analyzing collision avoidance radar for air traffic. Statisticians who had worked with NASA on the reliability of complex systems were involved in highway safety research. Econometric techniques which had been used to study how the national economy would operate in times of emergency were now being applied to building an input-output model of North Carolina's economy. Engineers who had developed oxygen-measuring devices for spacecraft now designed and built sensing equipment that monitored ozone concentrations near the earth's surface.

While these and other changes were gradual, not abrupt, and were based on market assessments of the professional and physical resources that RTI should be assembling, they weren't encouraged for revenue purposes alone, nor did RTI follow others' cues. They were pretty much made to happen, pretty well planned.

One important event in the planning process occurred at the end of May 1967, when the Institute management group—Herbert, Clark, Ashton, division directors, several senior scientists, some office heads—met at an off-campus site for a two-day retreat. Topics that had been agreed upon for discussion included a five-year growth plan (double the size of the Institute), organizational regrouping (consolidate the four engineering research laboratories), and matching the staff's varied and substantial talents with some of the problems and goals that could be expected to receive greater national attention in the years immediately ahead. Subjects on which consensus was reached included medicinal chemistry and other health-related programs, population research, regional economics, and environmental studies dealing primarily with air pollution's effects, abatement, and measurement.

Three years later, at the Board of Governors meeting in May of 1970, Herbert recalled aloud that "planning session in early 1967 at which Dr. Finkner made an impassioned and convincing argument that world-wide

* RTI research specifically related to what used to be called "the pill" was, to Wall's and Herbert's belief, the largest drug metabolism contract (not grant) supported by the National Institute of General Medical Science.

population expansion constituted a problem surpassing all others in importance and that research on population and family planning must be high on our list."

Within a year after Finkner's memorable declaration, RTI had two contracts in demography and had established working ties with UNC's Carolina Population Center. A year after that a population program was formally structured within the Statistics Research Division. And in the fall of 1971 a Center for Population Research and Services was created with Horvitz as its director, developing nations as its laboratory, and the U.S. Agency for International Development (USAID) as its chief client.

A few choices from a swarm of top-drawer domestic quality of life research projects will be too briefly touched upon in the next two chapters. What follows now is a detour abroad.

Going Overseas

From the time of Finkner's enunciation of a population research initiative, RTI's emphasis was on an improved quality of life as the most effective means for limiting births. This view holds that socioeconomic factors and fertility are linked, that as standards of living rise birth rates fall, that contraceptive methods are desirable, not to say essential, but that, over time, "development is the best pill."

RTI and the Carolina Population Center were not alone, but in the late sixties and early seventies they were among the few organizations stressing "the socioeconomic correlates of fertility." That is, they took the position that effective population control relies on aspects of national development that offer greater incentives to have fewer children, incentives such as more widespread educational opportunities and public health services, better sanitation and nutrition and medical care, increased labor productivity, a bigger role for women in the workplace. It's no accident that "Integrated Population and Development Planning" was the name of a decade-long RTI/USAID project that provided technical assistance on policy analysis and planning to 50 countries in all regions of the developing world, or that "Resources for Awareness of Population Impacts on Development" is the name of a later five-year USAID-funded policy and planning project.

A feature of RTI's development policy research has been its extensive training of Third World planners in microcomputer technology and specially tailored software that enables them to anticipate outcomes from efforts to meet the changing needs and goals and resources that are involved in addressing such population-related issues as housing, literacy, health care, land use, and sanitation and safe water supply.

When the Center for Population Research and Services was formed in 1971, most of its initial effort concerned fertility and mortality patterns, the cost-effectiveness of various family planning strategies, and the relationship that family planning and health services bore to economic and social development. The work centered on the population problems of countries in which the Near East and South Asia Office of USAID was active.

Within a year the center's geographic range had extended to include Taiwan, Korea, and West Africa, where Abraham S. David was in residence for four years as adviser to a population dynamics research and teaching program at the University of Ghana. An economist with his Ph.D. from N.C. State and a post-doctoral master's degree in public health from UNC, David had joined RTI in 1969.

Lois A. MacGillivray became director of a renamed Center for Population and Urban-Rural Studies in the summer of 1976. The name change reflected a growing interest at RTI in the technological and training needs of local governments in both the Third World and the U.S. MacGillivray, a sociologist with a Ph.D. from Carolina, signaled CPURS' new and broader base by continuing in a project role as supervisor of a six-year National Science Foundation analysis of fire protection service organization in medium-sized U.S. metropolitan areas.

David returned from Ghana that same summer and served within CPURS as coordinator of a 30-month RTI/USAID effort to help ministries of the government of Morocco plan and carry out measures for curbing the severe malnutrition that cursed that nation. With RTI's chief-of-party, agricultural economist Michael v.E. Rulison, in Rabat, the capital city, David looked after the necessary project communications and technical contacts between Rabat, USAID, RTI statistical and economics researchers, and UNC and N.C. State consultants in nutrition, plant science, transportation, and anthropology.

This experience demonstrated that nearly any overseas research would call upon more than one RTI center (Rulison was a senior staff member in state and regional planning), plus outside consultants, USAID staff, and host country professionals, so in 1977 David was named as head of a separate, coordinating Office for International Programs (OIP) while MacGillivray's center retained responsibility for the substance of most overseas work.

Further reorganization was to follow, as shown in Appendix II. For now: (1) David went to Nepal in 1980 on an RTI assignment of several years and was replaced by James S. McCullough, an urban planning (Ph.D. from UNC) and public finance specialist, who transferred from state and regional planning. During his decade as head of OIP, McCullough developed project work on four continents before going to Jakarta, Indonesia, in 1990 to run a four-year project on municipal management; and (2) toward the end of 1981 MacGillivray, a nun, became the president of her order's Holy Names College in California. She had built CPURS to a staff of 22, representing six social science disciplines. Her successor was Ronald W. Johnson, her center colleague for four years and a political science Ph.D. who had been a faculty member at Penn State for seven years.

Most of RTI's overseas research by far has dealt with population-related topics, but not all.

For example, RTI's very first international project, which took place in the fall of 1961, was a one-person appraisal of the feasibility of expanding the Nigerian government's work in the collection and analysis of data for an agricultural census. The person was senior statistician Walter A. Hendricks, and his finding was positive. Two years later a four-year USAID project began in which a three-person RTI team helped to set up and supervise a rural economic and agricultural statistics survey. Charles H. Benrud was chief-of-party until civil war in Nigeria prompted RTI to terminate the project and bring its staff home in the latter part of 1967. He is still active in sample allocation, frame construction, and sample selection for RTI surveys. J. Donald Bates, one of Benrud's assistants for the first two years, was manager of survey methodology and operations when he resigned from RTI in 1977.

Gertrude Cox had been a United Fruit Company consultant before RTI started. Early in her RTI career she again visited banana farms in Central America to aid company researchers in refining and confirming methods for making reliable crop production forecasts.

The Institute's third overseas project, announced in December 1961, was to have been the design of a household survey sample in Haiti, where two new vaccines against tuberculosis would be tested. The U.S. and Haitian sponsors were unable to come up with funding for the proposed human evaluation, and a cruise to Haiti for Finkner was the extent of RTI's participation.

More long-lived was a five-year project in Iran that began in 1967. RTI's primary activities were to transfer some of its civil defense expertise to that nation, and to prepare plans and procedures for organizing, equipping, and training the Iranian gendarmerie as a modernized civil police force that would operate largely in rural areas. In their recommendations on rural police mobility, RTI analysts took into account the widely varying geographic and climatic conditions in which the force would operate. For its members in some regions, snowmobiles were proposed. In others, camels would remain the best mode of transportation.

Technical and management assistance to host country planners was the purpose of a second project in Ghana. Specifically, RTI's Earl M. Brown, Jr., worked at the neighborhood and community level in Tamale, a city in northern Ghana, to help put action and execution behind plans for better health care services, better roads, drainage ditches, water supply, and other elements of the rapidly-growing city's infrastructure. This four-year effort was carried out under an RTI contract with USAID.

Another infrastructure project has been WASH, short for Water and Sanitation for Health, a USAID consortium whose members provide engineers, teachers, physicians, hygienists, and other specialists to assist developing nations to analyze water and sanitation (W&S) problems, to plan solutions, and to implement the plans. A consortium subcontractor since 1980, RTI has helped to measure the impact of W&S projects on public health, to teach farm and village populations about the reasons for the projects and the relationships between sanitation and health, and to train technicians in the installation, use, and maintenance of the physical facilities and equipment that serve to prevent disease by providing safe water.

Renewable energy is still another kind of multidisciplinary Third World development project that RTI has undertaken, specifically a five-year effort begun in 1982 to help the government of Morocco make the most of the oil-dependent country's renewable energy resources. Research disciplines involved in the USAID-funded study included electrical and mechanical engineering, economics, computer science, public administration, and electronics. RTI staff, under project director Henry P. Minis, Jr., and the Moroccan government's brand new renewable energy agency worked closely together to identify the more promising renewable energy sources—windmills and solar power to pump water, solar energy collectors to heat water, biogas technology to produce methane and fertilizers from biomass materials—and to design demonstration projects to promote national alternative energy policies and applications.

14. Skipping Through the Seventies

Among the issues being addressed or, more properly, readdressed as the 1960s became the 1970s, was a strengthening and broadening of Institute capabilities in environmental research. Two others that also draw brief comment were a renewed attention to interdisciplinary programs, and a fresh appraisal of opportunities for providing research to business and industry. Jim Worth figured in all three.

Emphasis on environmental research over and above the 1967 formation of the Engineering and Environmental Sciences Division was consistent with RTI's service goals. Public concerns about contaminated air's effects, and therefore about its causes and containment, were increasing apace, leading to the creation, in 1970, of the U.S. Environmental Protection Agency as the focus for federal research and regulatory activities.

During the previous autumn Worth had become coordinator for a committee that exerted an interdisciplinary influence on all of RTI's air pollution research. He and the committee, whose members were one or more senior scientists from each of RTI's five divisions, had plenty to consider. By the early seventies Institute research in the atmospheric sciences, on such topics as energy exchange processes in the ionosphere and ozone variability in mountainous terrain, had been transformed into comprehensive multidisciplinary studies that touched every RTI division.

Institute economists were heavily engaged, for example, in estimating the outlays necessary for compliance with air pollution legislation. Their projections covered the costs of controlling and reducing emissions of a growing list of gases and particulates from both mobile and stationary sources. The latter included virtually every basic industry in the nation, as well as commercial, institutional, and residential heating generators, and fossil-electric power plants. Related studies forecast the impact of pollution control costs on individual manufacturers, on consumer price levels, and on foreign trade balances.

Much effort also was devoted to reliable pollutant measurement methods, methods which for the most part didn't exist and had to be created by RTI and other participants in national interlaboratory programs. If air quality standards were to be enforceable, it was essential for the governmental, industrial, and scientific communities to have instruments and systems upon whose capacity for detecting, measuring, and recording pollutant levels all could agree and depend. Environmental methods testing, systems evaluation, and instrument development remain prominent activities at RTI twenty years later.

About a year after the Worth committee's formation, the interdisciplinary nature of RTI's commitment to the environmental sciences was strengthened when the committee was given responsibility for Institute-wide proposal development in the fields of air pollution, water pollution, solid wastes, and noise.

Soon enough its chairman had a new and very different assignment. This came about as the result of Herbert's decision to take a concerted crack at trying to build an expanded base of industrial and commercial clients. Accordingly, he asked Worth and Wortman to leave the research mainstream temporarily and devote most of their time to a detailed assessment of RTI's potential for increasing its industrial research volume, a figure that Herbert hoped might reach 25 percent of the Institute's annual total.

A year later, in January 1972, the "Industrial Research Study" was completed after discussion and visits with some twenty trade organizations and eighty corporations. Little came of the study's recommendations, which included patent development, recruiting industrially experienced researchers, and intensified marketing. By and large, the long-term development of relationships with potential industrial clients just wasn't among RTI researchers' priorities. In general, their backgrounds, their personal interests, and their professional preferences all favored governmental or academic research over the problem-oriented, new product, applied research needs of industry. A more widespread interest in industrial research was to emerge in the 1980s.

And there were competing priorities, as touched upon in the previous chapter. Foremost among these was the impulse, shared by RTI scientists and research managers alike, to devote their talents, energies, and time to the attainment of such national goals as better health care, better education, cleaner air and water, space exploration, defense, nutrition, drug abuse prevention. For a scientific institution, this predisposition toward quality of life concerns inevitably entailed research sponsorship by federal agencies.

Staff productivity and business considerations were also parts of the federal vs. commercial reckoning for, per unit of effort, the cost of marketing a research service to government is lower than it is to private industry. In his May 1989 report to the RTI board, by which time commercial activity had increased significantly, Herbert noted that "A far greater investment of time and patience is necessary to develop a relationship of trust and confidence with a potential commercial client than is required to match capabilities and experience with the research needs of federal agencies."

Another consideration was that RTI's commercial contracts during the 1970s infrequently exceeded $50,000, while federal research projects could routinely—but it sure wasn't always so—range into the hundreds of thousands and millions of dollars and cover many separate tasks. The differentials in cost and return exerted obvious influences on Institute profit centers.

One observation in the Worth-Wortman report reveals a notable characteristic of RTI operations. They wrote that "No matter how good a suggested concept or idea might be or how good the potential market . . . it is likely to fail if it does not have a strong champion in the Institute staff." They went on to point out that good ideas are most likely to be realized as projects, or programs, when the persons who generate and refine the ideas are also the persons who lead the research.

The notable characteristic revealed in this passage is that RTI did not develop as a from-the-top-down outfit. Except for Herbert's setting into motion the events that led to the several original research units, the RTI tradition has been that research initiatives are taken by the scientific staff. Those "successful ideas" identified by Worth-Wortman are successful only when concept and support originate in the technical leadership.

Chet Clark couldn't and didn't command RTI's atmospheric chemists to go to Cincinnati; instead, he "began pushing." When the scientists saw the opportunities that he had seen, and got interested, they went. An even better example involves high speed ground transportation. For six years in the 1960s Herbert sat on the technologically adventurous and influential U.S. Department of Commerce Technical Advisory Board. For two of those years he was chairman of its Panel on High Speed Ground Transportation, a post obviously replete with opportunities for matching high priority, high-tech R&D needs with the capabilities of RTI operations analysts, statisticians, and materials and mechanical engineers. Replete with opportunity, maybe, but Herbert couldn't rouse a spark of interest within RTI and finally gave up trying.

One thing he couldn't give up on, ever, was his obligation, and his wish, to provide North Carolina with the finest contract research institute possible, and in September of 1971 he faced an event that would profoundly affect this goal: the imminent departure of Clark, who had reached what was then the mandatory retirement age of 65.

Herbert began preparing for this change well in advance, and during the preceding March had scheduled a two-day, off-site strategy session of senior management. With typically broad outlook, Herbert's strategy didn't concern itself with Clark's replacement, but instead called for a candid look at the kinds of things RTI would want to be doing five years hence. Such an appraisal would suggest appropriate resolutions to the question of a Clark successor.

The management retreat produced no surprises, but its conclusions illustrated how greatly RTI's research interests had grown and changed in ten years: from reliance on projects in statistical analysis, radioisotopes, plant screening, civil defense, and solid state device fabrication to wide-ranging programs in health and medical-related research, environmental pollution and protection, education, population, semiconductor materials, drug abuse, technology utilization, electronic systems design and reliability, regional economics, air navigation and collision avoidance systems, and highway safety.

There was more to this versatility than the ability to identify and respond to shifting national research priorities. It was also the key to RTI's impressive business success during a period that *Chemical & Engineering News* weekly called "by and large a gloomy one" for the not-for-profit research institutes. During the summer of 1971, the magazine reported a combined three-year growth of 1.9 percent for the nine other not-for-profits.* For the same three years, RTI's growth was a sparkling 43 percent, attributed by Herbert to the emphasis on quality of life research, to the caliber of RTI scientists and their ability to perceive coming changes in the nation's R&D needs, and to cooperative ties with the founding universities. With 1971 contract volume of nearly $8.5 million, an increase of 12 percent over the previous year, RTI had become the fifth largest of the institutes.

By pointing toward RTI's research future, the management retreat discussions also enabled Herbert and the others to begin sketching out the general dimensions of a new organizational framework. Given where we intend to go, what's the best way to get there? Various alternatives were offered and examined throughout the summer by Herbert, Clark, Ashton, the division and laboratory directors, and Executive Committee members Hobbs, Little, and J. Lee Marsh, who was R&D vice president with Union Carbide Chemicals.

The structure finally decided upon encouraged interdisciplinary research and enhanced opportunities for contributing to national goals. Its main elements were three research groups, each to be headed by a vice president and each comprised of centers and divisions whose directors would be accountable for research performance, staffing, and program development.

In a series of meetings on September 3, 1971, Herbert emphasized to all segments of the staff that the research vice presidents would function as

* Franklin in Philadelphia; Denver at the university there; Battelle Northwest in Richland, Washington; and the six named in Chapter 6: Battelle Columbus, IITRI, Midwest, Southern, Stanford, and Southwest.

corporate officers concerned with total Institute operations, and not simply as division directors with blown-up titles. To underscore this "single Institute" thrust, the three groups weren't given official names. They were to be known as lower case group I, group II, and group III. Official or not, descriptive names were used in print and in conversation, and "group" inevitably attracted the capital G.

Finkner was group I vice president for social and economic systems and human resources. Monroe Wall was group II vice president for physical and life sciences. Worth was group III vice president, with Bob Burger as chief scientist, for environmental sciences and engineering.

Reporting to Finkner were Paul G. Homeyer, director for statistics; Horvitz, director for population studies; Eckerman, director for societal programs; Wakeley, director for health systems; and Street, head of state planning and regional development research. A center for educational research was also created, with Finkner as acting director until a permanent appointment could be made. Reporting to Worth were Jim Brown, director for technology applications, and Wortman, director for engineering. Worth and Harry L. Hamilton, Jr., headed an environmental studies center on an acting basis.

Both group I and group III were to experience additions, the former eventually counting ten centers. By 1978, group III's name had become energy, engineering and environmental sciences, and its four divisions (with directors Wortman, Tommerdahl, Ed Hill, and Brown) had 13 departments.

Group II's name, physical and life sciences, was adopted in anticipation of moving polymer research into Wall's group upon Anton Peterlin's retirement in two years. The group had but one division, chemistry and life sciences, with Wall retaining the director's title. In December four assistant directors were named: Ivy Carroll for organic and medicinal chemistry, Ed Cook for life sciences and bioorganic chemistry, Colin Pitt for physical sciences, and David W. Rosenthal for the mass spectrometry center.

Group I's new Center for Education Research and Evaluation (CERE) was an outgrowth of RTI's success in running the National Assessment of Educational Progress. To avoid controversial state-by-state comparisons, NAEP results were reported geographically only by four regions of the country—northeast, southeast, central, and west. However, officials and school executives in many states wanted similar, assessment-like data as a planning base for appraising and improving their own specific educational systems. Such assessments could be tailored to meet any state's individual needs and goals, and to reflect its distinctive economic and demographic circumstances. Over the years RTI conducted assessments for more than a dozen states as diverse as Florida, Maine, Minnesota, and Texas.

Finkner wasn't content with limiting CERE's activity to state assessments. He wanted to underscore the acronym's research and evaluation, but it took nearly two years for him to recruit a director to do it. The recruit was Junius A. Davis, a Columbia University Ph.D. in counseling psychology who had spent 12 years in research and administration with the Educational Testing Service. Finkner said of Davis that his "more than 20 years at the forefront of research and testing in such areas as the processes of higher education, the nature of student subcultures, and the educational needs of minority students will be a tremendous asset as we expand. . . ."

Along with the educational psychologists and analysts he brought in, Davis didn't wait long to begin delivering the substance that Finkner promised. Right off the bat, beginning in August 1973, was the first of a series of follow-ups to track down and question a huge sample of 22,000 young men and women who had been high school seniors in 1972. Known as the National Longitudinal Study, the follow-ups conducted for the U.S. Office of Education (not yet a department) were a massive effort to find out what happens to young adults after they leave high school, and how well their experiences there prepared them for work, or technical training, or college.

Coming soon after was the first of the evaluations of the federal Upward Bound program for disadvantaged high schoolers, studies that prompted Upward Bound officials to coin the respectful sobriquet of Mr. Upward Bound for RTI research psychologist Graham T. Burkheimer, Jr. A concurrent project was an assessment of Talent Search counseling programs for disadvantaged students and drop-outs. Later, a complex, multiyear study was undertaken to measure the effectiveness of educational programs for the children of migratory agricultural workers and fishermen. Among other research started during CERE's first decade were appraisals of the content and delivery of educational services for handicapped students and the design of programs aimed at motivating women and ethnic minorities to study for careers in science and engineering.

In delivering a January 1978 report to Congress, the U.S. Secretary of Health, Education and Welfare, Joseph A. Califano, Jr., stated, "Schools that should be centers of teaching and learning basic skills and functional literacy have become centers of danger and violence for teachers and students... The findings of this three-year study indicate that the dimensions of the school crime problem remain extremely serious." Back at RTI, project director David L. Bayless said, "If we have done anything to help keep kids out there safe and out of trouble and not be afraid, I couldn't ask for more." The *Violent Schools — Safe Schools* report they were both talking about began in 1975 as the first effort to collect extensive data on crime and misbehavior in schools on a nationwide basis.

RTI's "extensive" data collection effort (e.g., 14 million items of information, including questionnaire data from 23,895 teachers and 31,373 pupils, and 6,283 interviews with student victims) was undertaken by RTI statistics and survey research centers, not by CERE, but clearly qualifies as educational research and evaluation. The survey analysis, written by the National Institute of Education, acknowledged the thousands of reported and unreported incidents of assault, robbery, theft, and disruption, and the millions of dollars in annual school property losses, but drew a hopeful conclusion: "A firm, fair and consistent system for running a school seems to be a key factor in reducing violence. Where the rules are known, and where they are firmly and fairly enforced, less violence occurs."

The group I, group II, group III arrangement was in place for 12 years, from 1971 to 1983, but the three research vice presidents became four on July 1, 1974. This change was occasioned by a three-year leave of absence for Finkner, who was wanted for the post of associate director of the U.S. Bureau of the Census, a distinguished and deserved professional recognition. Deliberations by Herbert, Finkner, and the group I senior staff stressed preservation of the cohesiveness and the spirit of cooperation that marked RTI's research on social and economic systems and human resources. The realignment they settled on, and that was agreed to by the Board of Governors, was to replace Finkner with two vice presidents, one for the statistical sciences and the other for the social sciences, both of them operating within the "group I" mantle.

The new offices were filled by Horvitz and Eckerman, respectively. Fifteen months earlier, Horvitz had left RTI to accept appointment as full professor of biostatistics at UNC-Chapel Hill. Popular demand helped induce him back. In the 1971 reorganization, Eckerman had been named director of the Center for the Study of Social Behavior (CSSB) and now he also took on responsibility for the resource planning, educational, health systems, and population research centers. Following him as CSSB director was Al Cruze, promoted from Street's economic development center.

During Eckerman's tenure in CSSB he and his colleagues had added a new dimension to RTI's societal research, that of drug abuse. While it had long been assumed that drug abuse and criminal behavior went hand in hand, there was little documentation at the start of the 1970s on the actual percentage of all crime that was attributable to drug users, or on the types of crime in which they were involved. Specifically, behavioral scientists and law enforcement officials were concerned about the possibility that the nature of drug-related offenses was shifting from the petty larceny and vice that support a habit toward more serious crimes against the person, including homicide, rape, and aggravated assault.

Enter RTI's vaunted survey research capability, a couple of substantive procedural innovations, a U.S. Department of Justice contract, and a report on "Drug Usage and Arrest Charges" that was released in January 1973. Its authors were project director Eckerman, survey manager Don Bates, economist J. Valley Rachal, and senior statistician Ken Poole. The primary conclusion of their unprecedented study was that there was no evidence to indicate that drug users are more often involved in violent crimes than nondrug users. The study data and findings are still a valuable resource, but what may have greater interest to readers years later are the innovative procedures that Eckerman's research team proposed and carried out.

The most unusual was the collection of a urine specimen from survey participants and its analysis by thin layer chromatography to detect the presence of specified drug substances. About 300 men were examined at the central jail intakes in each of six cities: Brooklyn, Chicago, Los Angeles, New Orleans, San Antonio, St. Louis.* They were arrestees, not convicted individuals, and elaborate measures had to be taken to protect their anonymity: individuals' names did not appear on any questionnaire or urine container; interview questions did not delve into the nature of the act for which they'd been arrested, and did not ask about past criminal behavior. (RTI staff members were protected, too. Eckerman was the first researcher in the U.S. to obtain legal immunity from being compelled to reveal the names or other identifying characteristics of persons who are the subjects of a drug research study.)

Interviews with the arrestees asked about drug use history, health, and social and economic characteristics, but not about criminal records. The men included in the survey sample (they were all men) gave an exceptionally high degree of cooperation, especially considering the sites and the circumstances, with 92 percent of 1,889 respondents providing a urine specimen and 81 percent completing a personal interview. Most of those not interviewed had been released on bail prior to interviewer contact; of those contacted, only 3 percent refused to participate.

Drugs/crime wasn't the only substance abuse first for Eckerman's and Cruze's center during the 1970s. One of them, Rachal's survey of U.S. teenagers' drinking behavior, was released near the end of 1975 and drew national attention for its finding that nearly one-quarter of junior and senior high school students were heavy to moderately heavy drinkers.

* During interviews about the research over the next few years, Eckerman always emphasized that the study's data pertain to the six cities studied and those six cities only. They did not reflect a random sample of all arrestees throughout the country.

In another study, 12 years of effort that began in 1977 culminated in October 1989 with the publication of *Drug Abuse Treatment: A National Study of Effectiveness*, a book assessing the various treatment outcomes that was written by research psychologist Robert L. Hubbard and coauthors.* Their major conclusion was that, while it cannot guarantee a cure, treatment has met with notable success in reducing the rate of drug abuse and the demand for illegal drugs. The project was known at RTI as TOPS, for Treatment Outcome Prospective Study.

Or perhaps the project's culmination had occurred a couple of weeks earlier when President Bush used material from the book in a televised address about his administration's war-on-drugs strategy. The President forgot to mention RTI by name, but the printed version of his statement included two tables crediting RTI as their source.

Drugs of abuse also were a major topic of research in RTI chemistry laboratories throughout the 1970s, and still are. Efforts to develop a chemical profile of marijuana began in the late 1960s, a time when scientists knew relatively little about the plant and also a time when marijuana was by far America's most popular illegal drug.

Since then, Institute research into the chemistry, pharmacology, and biochemical mechanisms of abused substances has expanded to include cocaine, heroin, morphine, LSD, amphetamine, PCP (an abused anesthetic drug), narcotic antagonists such as methadone and, more recently, the highly potent synthetic compounds known as designer drugs.

One facet of RTI's pioneering research dealt with the development of new and more sensitive methods for detecting drugs in human tissue through the use of chromatography, mass spectrometry, and radioimmunoassay. These analytical techniques have proved useful in many biological studies at RTI and elsewhere, as well as in hospitals and forensic laboratories.

Institute scientists also discovered new methods for synthesizing abused drugs and their antagonists, and for labeling them with radioisotopes. These materials have been sent from RTI to medical centers throughout the world for use in pharmacological and toxicological studies.

Drug metabolism studies involved RTI chemists in many aspects of research from drug identification, synthesis, and labeling, to assistance with clinical evaluations of how a parent drug and its metabolites behave in the body. RTI was in the forefront of work to develop synthetic chemical procedures for obtaining marijuana's pure constituents, called cannabinoids,

* Mary Ellen Marsden, Rachal, Henrick J. Harwood, and Elizabeth J. Cavanaugh, all of RTI, and Harold M. Ginzburg of the federal Health Resources and Services Administration.

especially Delta-9-THC (short for tetrahydrocannabinol), the active compound responsible for marijuana's psychotropic, or mind-altering, effects. During the 1970s, RTI became particularly well known to the public for its contributions to research on the metabolic fate of cannabinoids in humans.

For example, in March of 1977 Monroe Wall was on the front pages and the evening news in Chicago, and on the national news wires elsewhere, with his testimony that an elevated train motorman had ingested marijuana prior to a crash that had killed 11 people. Wall was unable to pinpoint exactly when marijuana had been smoked, but RTI's analytical methods were even then so sensitive that the occurrence could have taken place several days earlier and Wall could still have identified a THC metabolite's presence in the motorman's urine sample.

Less welcome, more widespread, and longer lasting marijuana publicity had already broken in January, when a National Institute on Drug Abuse official spilled the beans about a contract under which RTI had been manufacturing marijuana cigarettes. News writers from coast to coast had a field day composing lead paragraphs about legal reefer rollers, and the term "joint research" was a favorite. (Also under a NIDA contract, the marijuana was grown at the University of Mississippi.)

For experiments with live subjects, it was essential to have cigarettes of uniform size and weight and of known cannabinoid content, requirements that called for them to be manufactured only under carefully controlled conditions. RTI's cigarettes and other dosage forms—capsules, tablets, ophthalmic liquids—have been distributed under NIDA auspices to government research and treatment programs all over the U.S., including those of the Institute's clinical collaborators at UNC-Chapel Hill.

# # #

Group III semiconductor research achievements, with principals such as Burger, Wortman, and others, attracted international attention to RTI throughout the 1970s, none more so than in the fall of 1978 when the U.S. Department of Energy's Sandia Laboratories announced that N.C. State University and RTI had designed and built a working monolithic cascade solar cell, a worldwide first that Sandia officials called a major step toward doubling the efficiencies attained by conventional, silicon solar cells. The new structure, resembling two solar cells stacked one on top of the other, "cascades" sunlight through its layers, thereby converting more of the solar spectrum into electricity than an ordinary solar cell can. The materials in the successful cascade solar cells are III-V compounds, three-five because they are made of elements in the third and fifth columns of the chemist's periodic table.

The cascade cell concept had been established long before, but the RTI/NCSU team was the first to demonstrate it. Two developments in the process may be noted. First, chronologically, was that after Dick Alberts joined RTI in 1975, he aided in recruiting Michael F. Lamorte. More than ten years earlier the two had a brief solar cell connection when the Air Force Avionics Laboratory (AFAL), where Alberts then worked, sponsored III-V solar cell manufacture at RCA, where Lamorte was manager of photosensitive device engineering. He became convinced that a cascade cell was feasible.

Meanwhile, scientists at RTI and the Triangle universities had begun moving to the forefront of microelectronics research. In 1976 they set up an informal cooperative program for basic investigations of III-V materials as the basis for devices that would surpass silicon technology capabilities in speed, frequency, and power, while also allowing reductions in size and weight. They named their program the Center for the Synthesis and Study of Semiconductor Compounds (CSSSC, pronounced seasick), and tagged Wortman as its first director. CSSSC discussions led to AFAL funding for a study of the structures and III-V materials that might lead to a new generation of devices for converting sunlight into electricity. Principals in the effort were N.C. State University's John R. Hauser, a former RTI staff member, and Michael A. Littlejohn. RTI's Mayrant Simons declines credit for any scientific contribution, but held technical management responsibilities as project leader. CSSSC refined the cascade cell concept into theory, then into design, and then brought it to developmental stages at RTI's Bacon Street Annex. Here, success in the laboratory was achieved by chemists, engineers, and technicians under Salah M. Bedair, an RTI electrical engineer who later became an NCSU professor. Bedair's leadership in developing techniques to grow and utilize novel solar cell structures came to fruition with the fabrication of the first working devices of their kind.

Demonstration of the cascade solar cell was, in the energy conscious '70s, a cause for optimism about a practical new source of electric power, as well as the cause of considerable governmental and news media interest. Concurrently, RTI solar energy research expanded into the costs and market potential of intermediate-load solar power applications for such establishments as commercial and service businesses, schools, hospitals, and small industry. Interest in the cascade solar cell never ceased entirely (see next chapter) and by the end of the 1980s was being rejuvenated under Michael L. Timmons, manager of semiconductor materials research. (It's notable that Timmons' first job after college was as an RTI junior chemist analyzing constituents of marijuana. He later obtained B.S., M.S., and Ph.D. degrees in electrical engineering.)

Other energy-related research during the '70s decade included methods for converting coal to gas and liquid fuels, solar heating and cooling, variations in solar radiation levels as influenced by features such as sea breezes and coastal geography, estimating the total energy required for the manufacture and distribution of hundreds of industrial and consumer products, and forecasting the energy consumption effects that would result from a national system of including refundable 5-cent deposits in the purchase price of bottles and cans used for beer and soft drinks.

Generally speaking, energy-related research other than solar cell development and coal processing called upon the increasingly visible research talents that had already begun to be assembled at RTI for environmental programs. Notable skills and solid environmental research accomplishments for the EPA, industrial groups, and private companies were particularly evident in group III's Systems and Measurements Division under Tommerdahl, group II's Analytical Sciences unit under Edo D. Pellizzari, and group I's Sampling Research and Design and Survey Operations Centers under Chromy and R. Paul Moore, respectively. A very short list:

— Design automated and manual techniques for monitoring atmospheric pollution and for source testing methods;

— Evaluate flue gas and industrial waste gas cleaning methods for controlling particulate and sulfur oxide emissions in copper, zinc, and lead smelting processes;

— Examine the economic effects of a pollution tax on industrial emissions;

— Investigate the ties between urban hydrocarbon control strategies and high ozone concentrations in rural areas;

— Develop sorbent materials for capturing organic pollutant vapors from the air for subsequent analysis;

— Combine in-depth pattern recognition techniques with statistical studies to correlate airborne pollutant concentrations with human health effects;

— Conduct on-site and in-transit ambient air surveys in cities and rural areas throughout the U.S. (RTI's mobile environmental monitoring laboratory was purchased and equipped with the assistance of grants from the N.C. Board of Science and Technology.);

— Monitor community health surveillance systems to determine the effects of nitrogen oxides on human respiratory infections.

Intergroup participation was a mark of many environmental research projects, and still is. Near the end of the 1970s and throughout the 1980s RTI's multidisciplinary capabilities came together most noticeably in the multi-million-dollar Total Exposure Assessment Methodology (TEAM) studies for the EPA. They are discussed briefly in the next chapter.

# # #

For brief discussion now are a mere three more from the dozens and dozens of projects going on at RTI during the 1970s. One is completed, and another is being tested in clinical demonstrations.

The third has a good chance of never being fully realized, despite the highest hopes, thousands of arduous hours, great human interest, and substantial investments by RTI, the National Institutes of Health, NASA, and the Veterans Administration. Nevertheless, it's well worth your time. It's the autocuer.

Biomedical engineer Robert L. Beadles' younger daughter was born deaf, a discovery her parents made when she was 18 months old. Babies stricken before they learn the spoken language grow up especially susceptible to intellectual and emotional problems; they almost never learn to read beyond the fourth-grade level. Beadles resolved that these prospects weren't good enough, but not until 1970, when Elena was three, did he chance upon a televised "Today Show" segment on which something called cued speech was being explained by its originator, Orin Cornett of Gallaudet University for the deaf. Eight hand symbols held at four different positions by a speaker's face enable a deaf person to distinguish between words and syllables that would look identical to a lipreader. For example, some 60 words in English look like "met" to a lipreader, but when lipreading is supplemented by the hand symbols, or cues, each of the 60 words can be identified.

The Beadles family learned cued speech and Elena made great strides in English and her other schoolwork, but Beadles was aware of a severe limitation: as with sign language, the deaf person who relies on cued speech can communicate easily only with others who know the method. Engineer Beadles began thinking about the possibility of a wearable device that could electronically analyze a speaker's voice and automatically produce visual cues for the lipreader.

Cornett had had a similar idea for what he dubbed an autocuer, but the electronics expertise he lacked wasn't available to him until Beadles and RTI became his collaborators along a broad research front of optics, linguistics, computerized speech analysis, and teaching techniques.

After years of technical victories and funding shortfalls, Beadles's team by the mid-1980s had engineered an autocuer weighing about a pound. It consists of special eyeglasses and a box, worn at the belt, little larger than a pack of cigarettes. The box houses a microcomputer that analyzes speech signals received from two tiny microphones set into the eyeglass frame. The microcomputer converts these signals into electronic symbols that are fed into a light-emitting diode display in one of the eyeglass lenses. With slight movements of the head, the deaf person wearing the glasses can "see" speech in the form of cues that appear to flash near the speaker's mouth, thus providing the desired supplement to lipreading. Preliminary testing of the device by Gallaudet students yielded promising returns about its convenience in use and its enhancement of student comprehension.

But. More technical victories are needed before full-scale field testing can attempt to demonstrate the autocuer's effectiveness. An assured source of funding for commercial development is needed. Questions remain about power supply, program memory, and about commonly agreed-upon standards for the practice of cued speech. But the autocuer doesn't have to be a sure thing to be a great thing.

# # #

Among the researchers hired in the early days of autocuer development was Blake S. Wilson, a brand new electrical engineering graduate of Duke University. After a year or so he became project director of a study to determine the fundamental interaction mechanisms between microwave energy and biological systems. The study, undertaken in collaboration with a Duke neurophysiologist and a Duke EE professor, might reveal new information about microwave radiation safety levels and might also establish the potential for a hearing prosthesis.

Their approach called for the monitoring of single fibers in the auditory nerve of a laboratory animal that had been exposed to microwave radiation. Wilson suggested—it was his idea—that if the interactions between microwave and auditory system took place at the hair cell or neural level, there would be important evidence of the potential for stimulating functional portions of profoundly deaf persons' auditory systems, a potential beyond the reach of conventional hearing aids.

Fifteen years later, as the 1990s open, announcements of international import are on the horizon concerning the speech processing strategies that Wilson and his colleagues have developed to improve the performance of cochlear implants, surgically-implanted devices that stimulate deaf persons' auditory nerves and that can dramatically improve their ability to understand speech.

During these years Wilson has firmly and consistently rejected all entreaties and enticements to progress academically beyond the bachelor's degree. He compensates through his efforts as an adjunct member of the Duke University Medical Center otolaryngology faculty, as a founding force and auditory prosthesis research director of the Duke/RTI Center for the Hearing Impaired, and as coordinator of the several speech processing research and evaluation activities conducted by RTI scientists and by surgeons and other clinicians at Duke and the University of California at San Francisco. In 1983 Wilson was named to head RTI's neuroscience research office, whose other programs include hearing aids that process speech, full speech recognition by automated acoustic and visual processing, and concepts for telephone communications for the deaf.

# # #

NMCES, pronounced Nemesis, was a mind-boggler. This was the National Medical Care Expenditure Study, fully deserving all its many descriptors, of which a sample would include colossal, complex, formidable, unique and, an RTI favorite, unprecedented.

NMCES was conceived and launched, in 1976, in an attempt to meet what Horvitz termed the "insatiable appetite" for information about the micro components of Americans' health care picture, namely, what medical services are used, who uses them, how much they cost, and who eventually pays the bills. The five-year, $22 million project was sponsored by the National Center for Health Services Research and the National Center for Health Statistics.

The volume of medical care data collected was huge, some 4.5 billion characters. Subsequent analyses by the clients and other government, university, and private organizations would address major policy issues relating to the delivery and funding of health care, alternative programs for national health insurance (wanted by President Carter) that might come before Congress, and the effects that Medicare and Medicaid were having on access to and the use and cost of health care. The data were easily the most comprehensive body of information ever assembled (not so easily) on the health care of the U.S. population.

The study had three major elements: (1) A survey of 13,500 randomly selected families whose 36,000 members were interviewed six times over a 15-month period in 1977-78. Interview frequency, once every 13 weeks, was intended to reduce errors caused by failure to recall each and every visit to a doctor, health care facility, or pharmacy. Another memory aid was a specially designed calendar for recording these visits. (2) A survey of the physicians, hospitals, and clinics that provided care to the respondents. A sample of about

60 percent of these 22,000 different physicians and 4,500 different hospitals and clinics was surveyed to verify information obtained in the family interviews about the date and purpose of each visit, diagnosis, major procedures performed during a hospital stay, and total costs and sources of payment associated with each visit. (3) A survey of the employers and insurance companies responsible for respondents' health insurance coverage, including questions about type of coverage, premiums, and source of payment. Contacts with health care providers, employers, and insurers were made only with the written permission of the family survey participant.

No project had ever been such an all-consuming experience for such a large part of RTI. On any given day 125 or more statistical sciences staff members could be working on NMCES, to say nothing of several hundred temporary telephone, field interviewer, and data services employees. Also engaged in the study as subcontractors to RTI were the National Opinion Research Center, a University of Chicago survey affiliate that did about half of the family interviews, and Abt Associates, a Cambridge, Mass., firm with experience in health care provider and insurance company studies.

A special feature of the NMCES contract was the clients' requirement that Horvitz devote full time to the study for its first 30 months. During this time Eckerman took on both halves of the group I administrative load.

15. Skimming Across the Eighties

NMCES and its companion survey NMCUES are convenient carryovers that began in the mid-and late '70s, respectively, and extended into the '80s. NMCUES, acronym for the National Medical Care Utilization and Expenditure Study, was a near match for NMCES' magnitude and complexity; at just under $20 million, a bit cheaper.

"We will again be coping with several billion items of information," said project leader Horvitz of the mammoth survey design, data collection, recording, and reporting tasks that would occupy him and scores of others for almost three years. Despite best efforts, NMCES had not stayed the government's "insatiable appetite" for information about America's health care needs and services, or for data essential for evaluating various proposals for national health insurance.

NMCES and NMCUES were much alike in their aims of finding out the extent to which Americans used available health care services, how much those services cost, and who paid the bills.

Among the differences, three stood out: (1) NMCUES data were collected for 1980, NMCES data for 1977. The three-year interval was of significant assistance to the National Center for Health Statistics in assessing trends in health care user characteristics, the variety of services they required, and costs and methods of payment. The agency needed such data for monitoring health insurance and cost containment programs. (2) NMCUES gave much greater emphasis to Medicare and Medicaid than NMCES had, thus helping to meet the Health Care Financing Administration's primary objective of gaining knowledge about health service use and cost patterns among enrollees in these programs. The NMCUES national sample of 6,000 was less than half the size of the earlier survey's, but also embraced an additional 1,000 Medicaid-eligible families in each of four populous states—California, Michigan, New York, and Texas. (3) NMCES had obtained verifying and supplementary information from physicians, hospitals, clinics, employers, and insurers. The later survey did not. It did, however, obtain care and cost data on the claims submitted to Medicare and Medicaid by survey participants.

As with NMCES, management depth was a most convenient asset for RTI in the successor NMCUES project. Finkner had returned to RTI from the

Census Bureau in mid-1977 and was elected to the new position of senior vice president. His initial concerns were for quality control and long-range planning, and he also had line oversight of international research. With Horvitz committed full-time to NMCUES for most of 1980, Finkner took over statistical sciences' administration. When Horvitz returned to his vice president's duties that winter, day-to-day direction of NMCUES was taken for 2½ years by Bob Thornton and, for the final two years, by Barbara A. Moser.

Not so convenient at all was a combination of factors that included the scheduled end of NMCES early in 1981 and the transfer of NAEP to another contractor, the imminent winding down of NMCUES, the new Reagan administration's slowing of energy research, including solar, its delays in funding contracts that had been awarded but not signed, and a plainly evident softening in the social sciences research market, particularly for the evaluation of innovative educational and welfare programs.

While the 1980s were a wonderfully productive decade for RTI in almost every way—scientific excellence, contributions to quality of life, business growth—the combination of circumstances just mentioned signaled a couple of rough years coming up. (See charts on annual revenue and staffing levels, Appendix I.)

More than once over the years Herbert had cautioned his Board of Governors and the senior staff that RTI could not consider itself immune to the operating fluctuations encountered by most businesses. Typical of his cautions was his emphasis to the board at the November annual meeting in 1981 "that a growth line without interruptions is an anomaly, that the history of any enterprise (whether measured by revenue, income, or employees) normally is represented by a curve which cycles around a growth line . . . that RTI, too, is subject to the natural laws of growth and that when our curve pauses, or cycles, it should not be seen as a signal for alarm or panic. The sun will still rise in the east, Duke and Carolina will play the last game of the season, and the *Commerce Business Daily* will be published tomorrow."

This time, his listeners heard him.* And if they hadn't paid heed earlier, there may have been sufficient reason. Not even counting the scientific staff's accomplishments, or the Institute's prominence as centerpiece of the re-

* In RTI's early years, staff would gather with Herbert for previews of his remarks at annual Board of Governors meetings, held in November. Soon the staff became too large for such gatherings, and in later years verbatim copies of Herbert's report to the board were distributed to all staff members on the morning of the day the annual board meeting took place.

nowned RTPark, RTI was a downright impressive business success. Why, just a year earlier, in November 1980, Herbert had reported a revenue of $47 million for the year, a jump of more than 40 percent above the $33 million in 1979, and had predicted further growth to $53 million in fiscal 1981.

The difference between November 1980's glowing report and November 1981's cautionary lecture was that, after 22 years, RTI's growth curve had finally been interrupted. The scheduled completion and near-completion of large contracts, unexpected funding delays in others, and program and budget uncertainties within several client agencies put the Institute's business cycle into the down mode for the first time.

Quickly, too. "Never in my memory," continued Herbert in his November 1981 board statement, "have national priorities been turned topsy-turvy as suddenly as they have during the past year."

The effect on RTI staff levels had been immediate, with 33 individuals being let go in March 1981 from social and statistical sciences, mostly junior researchers and analysts, but several senior, long-term employees, too. By year's end 22 others were released from group I and from administration and services, leaving the number of regular staff members at 987.

Such personnel cutbacks were a new experience for RTI, a traumatic one, according to Herbert. Of course, dismissals for cause or below-par performance had been made, but these weren't out of the ordinary for any employer. Involuntary terminations due to lost projects or shifts in agency funding had been extremely rare, and RTI usually went beyond routine good-conscience efforts to reassign those affected. Little solace came from knowing that other research organizations were suffering even severer hits during this period. The 1981 actions were a shock.

Some of the people released were understandably resentful, several of them speaking out publicly through the local media. The terminations surprised news-reading Triangle area citizens who had grown accustomed to thinking of RTI as invulnerable.

"While the firing of even a single individual is a painful decision," in Herbert's words, the 33 dismissals in March of 1981 represented less than 3 percent of the total staff. New hires in 1981 and 1982 totaled 219, but two years of dismissals, normal turnover throughout the Institute, and deliberate slowness in filling many vacancies caused the number of regular employees to drop from 1,088 at September 30, 1980, to 987 on the same date in 1981, and to 837 a year later. In the same two years the cuts took place, research revenues also decreased, from a high of $47.1 million in 1980 to $46.3 million in 1981 and to $41.3 million in 1982. In 1983 the staff total increased by an even 100, revenue was $41.5 million, and both growth curves have been up ever since.

The 1981-82 down years didn't seriously threaten RTI's stability, for if changes in federal priorities after President Reagan took office in January 1981 were to give RTI immediate headaches, there would also be opportunities ahead.

Increased spending by the Department of Defense was the most obvious. RTI expectations centered on very large scale integrated (VLSI) circuits, and on concepts for self-testing circuits in DoD's Very High Speed Integrated Circuit (VHSIC) program. VHSIC-related projects for the Navy and for DoD contractors such as the Hughes Aircraft Company had already begun in Tommerdahl's division under digital systems research supervisor James B. Clary.

Emphasis on defense and engineering technology was likely to be a stimulant for industrial innovation. Herbert resolved to renew the pursuit of industry clients.

A third and renewed area of opportunity was the U.S. Agency for International Development, whose new administrator promised a shift that would decrease transfer of capital to Third World countries and increase institution building, which is precisely what Finkner, Horvitz, and others at RTI and UNC-Chapel Hill had pushed and promoted for years.

1981's decisions to cultivate industrial and defense clients were soon justified. In the year the efforts started, the two categories together accounted for only 7.7 percent of the Institute's research revenue. An outside hope was that their combined total might rise to 20 percent in 1984. For the 1983 fiscal year, their combined total was 19.2 percent. A few examples will be coming along shortly to show how these gains were made.

Meanwhile, new research opportunities were being defined, successful proposals were refilling the contract pipeline, staff and revenue figures were recovering, capital resources were being restored, and by the end of 1982 Herbert had some corporate organizational issues to begin thinking about.

Finkner's retirement had already been delayed and he wanted to leave at the end of the next business year, September 30, 1983. That was also the date that Wall wanted to move from the group II vice presidency to a chief scientist position. Worth resigned on December 1, 1982.

(A group III change had occurred in the fall when Burger and Alberts left to take two of the three senior technical positions with the new Semiconductor Research Corporation. SRC president Larry W. Sumney held the third, taking the new post from his position in the Defense Department as head of the VHSIC program. Burger and Alberts had helped Sumney prepare the SRC blueprint that won him the job. SRC is a not-for-profit cooperative whose members are companies engaged in the manufacture or use of semiconductor integrated circuits. It coordinates and sponsors research primarily at universities. SRC's location in the Research Triangle Park can be attributed partially both to Sumney's desire to recruit Burger and Alberts and to RTI's provision of initial space, furnishings, and administrative services.)

With Worth gone, Finkner going, and Wall returning to full-time research, a review and examination of RTI resources and goals was in order. While involving the other officers, as well as division directors and senior scientists, Herbert and Finkner were the principal examiners, as they were later to be the principal planners. The process and the prospect were seriously hampered by Eckerman's death in June 1983.

By then, however, the principles guiding Herbert, Finkner, and the others had been settled on. The most important by far was that their organizational design should not be tailored specifically for the new 1983-84 business year, or even for 1984-85, but should be regarded as a first step toward the decade's end and the new generation of top leadership it would bring. "That generation of leadership exists within the Institute," Herbert emphasized to the Board of Governors, "and there should be no need . . . to turn outside to fill organizational boxes vacated in the future."

One of the boxes he meant was his own, and he meant what he said. Six years later, when he announced his decision to step aside as president, he made it clear to the board and the search committee that if his successor was not selected from within he, Herbert, might not step aside. He was asserting a point of principle, not threatening, but the assertion wasn't an idle one.

The management structure that emerged on October 3, 1983, was entirely new. For the first time RTI had an executive vice president with line responsibility for Institute-wide research operations. Reporting to him, instead of to Herbert, were ten research vice presidents, each responsible for a multidisciplinary unit's program and staff. It was a well-seasoned group. Executive vice president Horvitz had nearly 19 years at RTI, the research vice presidents averaged 17, ranging from Tommerdahl's 23 to Ron Johnson's 6. The organization shown in Appendix II reflects changes made subsequent to 1983; the lineup of unit vice presidents at that time was, alphabetically: Jim Brown, biomedical engineering, geosciences, technology applications; Jim Chromy, survey and computing sciences; Ed Cook, chemistry and life sciences; Al Cruze, economic and social systems; Johnson, public policy and international development; Forest Mixon, chemical engineering; Edo Pellizzari, analytical sciences; Ken Poole, statistical methodology and analysis; Tommerdahl, environmental sciences and engineering; and Tom Wooten, electronics and systems. The new organization returned Wooten to research endeavors after eight years in administrative positions as vice president and executive assistant to the president.

Research momentum in several subject areas had built up substantially prior to reorganization. One of them was semiconductors, although contract commitment lagged behind scientific commitment. James A. Hutchby came to RTI from NASA in 1980 as semiconductor research director and set about establishing the Institute and collaborators at N.C. State as a national center for III-V compound semiconductor research, emphasizing the advantages that materials such as gallium arsenide (GaAs) held over silicon. Major applications for III-V materials included integrated circuits, opto-electronics, and photovoltaics. RTI was active in all three, and was contributing state-of-the-art advances despite funding cuts. Beginning in 1984 the scientific commitment by Hutchby and others began to pay off, and soon enough RTI was once again recognized worldwide for its research leadership in military, space, and commercial applications of semiconductor technologies.

RTI semiconductor research received a major boost following President Reagan's call for a Strategic Defense Initiative (SDI) intended to place into space an electronic warning and defense network to detect and destroy enemy missiles before they could inflict damage. SDI, known to many as Star Wars, stirred more than passing political and scientific controversy. No political controversy, however, followed SDI's 1986 decision to award an initial three-year, $5.8 million contract to RTI to grow single crystal diamond film for use in very high speed electronic devices that would have to deliver large amounts of power, survive high temperatures, and withstand intense radiation. What did follow the SDI contract award announcement, however, was a lot more publicity and news media inquisitiveness than research manager Robert J. Markunas had ever experienced.

As science, if not as publicity, the work by Markunas and his associates is second to none for developing semiconductor quality diamond and testing its physical and electrical properties. Institute semiconductor researchers demonstrated a diamond electronic device in 1990, making RTI one of the first to have planar device technology in synthetic diamond film.

III-V materials, the cascade solar cell, and diamond semiconductor technology were among the engineering sciences research that RTI was undertaking for Department of Defense agencies, but they by no means represented the boundaries of RTI's work for armed services commands. Consider such other activities as support to the Navy in assessing underwater environmental effects on the propagation of acoustic signals, advanced cockpit navigational displays for the Air Force, water quality modeling for the Corps of Engineers, investigations of antimalarial primaquine analogs for the Army's Walter Reed Medical Center, comprehensive environmental chemistry data collection to aid the Air Force in complying with the Clean Air Act, and the preparation of blind-labeled test samples to help assure the reliability of drug-testing laboratories used by the military forces. In conjunction with all three Triangle universities, RTI managed an integrated fault tolerance research program that explored inexpensive built-in-test techniques to detect and localize malfunctioning components in complex military electronic systems. Position papers, most of them written by Burger, dealt with issues such as the nation's defense technology base, VHSIC, and assessments of the roles of various DoD electronic R&D laboratories.

Defense needs in the '80s also had a strong influence in rallying the social science and survey research activity that had taken such a battering at the decade's start.

Fourteen men were killed in a May 1981 plane crash aboard the aircraft carrier USS Nimitz. Autopsies showed traces of marijuana in the blood of six of them. The tragedy focused national attention on the problem of drug abuse among military personnel, and the armed forces' antidrug programs were quickly pushed through the planning stages and put into action. The DoD retained RTI to assess the programs' effectiveness, and the result, released late in 1983, was the second biennial Worldwide Survey of Alcohol and Nonmedical Drug Use Among Military Personnel. The innovative and complex study produced generally encouraging results, with findings showing that the percentage of military personnel using any nonmedical drug during the 30-day survey period dropped from the 27 percent recorded in 1980 to the 19 percent reported by RTI for 1982. Alcohol abuse, however, had risen, particularly among young, single, less educated males in the lower enlisted ranks.

If the survey was innovative and complex, it was also comprehensive. A 20-page, 105-question survey instrument was completed by 21,936 officers and enlisted personnel at 21 stateside and 37 overseas military installations. Data collection took place at military bases in South Korea, Japan, Okinawa, the Philippines, Guam, Italy, Germany, Greece, and the United Kingdom, as well as in the U.S.

RTI's next worldwide survey, in 1985, found that while alcohol use patterns remained relatively stable there was another dramatic decline in the prevalence of drug use to about 9 percent. Project leader Robert M. Bray, a senior social psychologist who also directed the earlier survey, attributed the drop to the deterrent effects of the military's "highly successful" urinalysis program. This second survey also found that substance users engage less often than nonusers in good health practices such as adequate exercise, proper nutrition and sleep habits, maintaining proper weight, and not smoking.

Bray was also the project leader for RTI's third survey in 1988. Only 5 percent of survey participants reported nonmedical drug use, and this time the figures for drinking and smoking were also down. "These findings are good news for the military," Bray said when survey results were released in 1989. "The military's policies on smoking, alcohol and other drug use, and promotion of healthy life styles appear to be working."

Like RTI's other major social surveys in health and educational fields, these studies of substance abuse in the military provided rich data sets to support further research and analysis.

Beginning in 1983, and throughout the rest of the decade, the Department of Defense also retained RTI for the annual Youth Attitude Tracking Study, conducted in later years by CATI, computer-assisted-telephone interviewing. The first YATS survey had been carried out by another contractor in 1975, two years after the military draft ended and DoD reliance on voluntary enlistments began. The goal of YATS is to produce a current and reliable assessment of the attitudes, motivations, intentions, backgrounds, and enlistment and career preferences of the young men and women the military services seek to enlist. Such information assists the services to formulate and target effective recruiting efforts to meet their manpower requirements.

Army efforts to positively influence soldiers' decisions to remain in the service, and to increase their readiness to fulfill Army job responsibilities, rely heavily on the success of support programs for soldiers' families. The effect that family factors have on soldier retention and readiness is the subject of a five-year, $10 million study that began at RTI early in 1987. Family factors being examined include stability, health, housing, schools, spouse employment, and many others. Among the research techniques being used are personal interviews, CATI, site visits, focus groups, and the convening of expert panels. With Rachal as overall supervisor, Cruze was the initial project director. After he took office as RTI's executive vice president in January of 1989, Janet Griffith assumed his project duties.

A convenient bridge between DoD projects and research for industry is ADAS, RTI's Architecture Design and Assessment System. Conceived at the start of the 1980s, by principal computer scientist Geoffrey A. Frank, as a tool with which DoD agencies could assure that proposed computer systems would do what they were supposed to do, ADAS was, by the end of the decade, a leading computer-aided engineering tool for the simultaneous design of computer hardware and software. Digital systems research director Clary and ADAS product development manager Deborah L. Franke found a ready market for this innovative method of designing electronic systems. By the time a licensing agreement for commercial sales was signed in December 1988, RTI's own demonstration and marketing efforts had already placed ADAS software at more than 65 DoD, NASA, and corporate laboratories, including Honeywell, RCA, Raytheon, TRW, and other firms.

Industry-sponsored research burgeoned right along with DoD contracts in the 1980s. It may never reach the 25 percent total revenue that Herbert had mentioned in 1971 as a possibility, but even so commercial customers accounting for a 10-15 percent share of research revenue and 30-40 percent of each year's projects provide a far better balance to RTI's client spectrum and to its service orientation than the near-negligible amounts of earlier years.

Several factors contributed to this positive trend. For one, greater experience in dealing with private companies bred greater confidence in the ability to do so; small or large, successful projects go a long way toward building those "relationships of trust and confidence" that Herbert had spoken of. Such relationships, in turn, are the key to the repeat business that's bread and butter for any supplier. Trust and confidence have been cultivated by staff members who have come to RTI from industrial research settings, and who readily identify with the technical problems and the time and money constraints facing their private sector peers. Manufacturing engineers, industrial chemists, and machinery designers have helped create commercial markets for RTI research ranging from chemistry to economics and from statistics to electronics. An additional assist early in 1983 was the inauguration of a one-person function dedicated to supporting marketing (supporting, not directing) in the private sector.

Research for business and industry brings with it the client's privilege to declare the results proprietary, and RTI's obligation to hold them at whatever level of confidentiality the client wishes. The following several paragraphs comment on some of the privately-sponsored research of the 1980s that the client publicized or gave its permission for RTI to do so.

If the Reagan administration was unconcerned about energy conservation and energy supply, the electric utility industry was very concerned. RTI experiments on the effect that alternate rate structures have on the demand for electricity had been going on since the mid-'70s for the U.S. Department of Energy, Blue Ridge Electric Membership Corp., and Carolina Power & Light Co. Economics director Allen K. Miedema and his RTI associates were recognized as a prime research resource for individual electric utility companies, for the N.C. Alternative Energy Corporation, and for industry associations such as the Electric Power Research Institute (EPRI).

Much of RTI's research has involved incentives for utility customers to avail themselves of time-of-use (TOU) prices, which are higher during periods of peak demand and lower when demand is low. If companies could devise measures to flatten the demand curve, they could avoid or delay the costs and environmental problems involved in building new generating plants. TOU incentives and related load management research has been carried out for EPRI, Dominion Resources, Inc., New York State Gas & Electric Co., Potomac Electric Power Co., and others.

Energy-efficient home appliance promotion analyses were performed for Florida Power & Light and Niagara Mohawk Power. Clients for studies of least-cost generating options include Southern California Edison, Duke Power, and Dominion Resources. During 1989, electric utilities were sponsors of 17 projects at RTI, ten of them new, including engineering and economic analyses of new technologies for power production and environmental protection.

Johnson & Johnson was in the vanguard of American companies offering comprehensive health promotion programs to their employees. J&J's trademark "Live for Life" program offered (and continues to offer) resources for employees who want to lead healthier lives through such measures as smoking cessation, weight loss, better diet, more exercise, buckling up, reduced stress. Results included healthier lifestyles, fewer diseases, and better morale among employees; greater productivity, less absenteeism, reduced health care costs, and a sense of accomplishment for J&J. Rather than rely on observation and intuitive measures of the success that "Live for Life" was having, Johnson & Johnson hired RTI to formally evaluate the program's impact. The J&J corporate organization was ideal for this purpose, embracing a number of semi-autonomous companies. Of the nine selected for RTI's study, "Live for Life" was being implemented at four, but had not yet been made available at the others. The study designed by RTI survey and statistical scientists called for gathering baseline health and lifestyle data from enrolled employees at the four "Live for Life" sites, and then repeating the data collection process after one year and two years of employee participation. On the same schedule, similar information was obtained from employees at the five comparison sites. In 1984, J&J's scientific coordinator wrote that "the treatment cohort . . . consistently shows greater improvements . . . this is pioneering work in an area where potential benefits have been difficult to measure with existing systems and methods." As the new decade began, RTI was still active in "Live for Life" research.

Scarcely a stranger to pioneering, RTI would soon lead a four-year U.S. Department of Health and Human Services project to develop guidelines by which company managers could accurately evaluate wellness programs' success in increasing productivity and/or reducing costs associated with absenteeism, hospitalization, disability, job turnover, unnecessary illness, and premature death.

Water supply has been a research topic at RTI for more than two decades, going back to the 1960s with Anton Schindler's Dreyfus Laboratory work with reverse osmosis membranes for seawater desalination. Since then, water-related studies by chemists, economists, engineers, and statisticians have been undertaken for assorted branches of the EPA, for the U.S. Fish and Wildlife Service, the Corps of Engineers, and for several municipalities, including the Research Triangle cities of Durham and Raleigh. An analysis of tap-water samples taken near Niagara Falls was but one of several chemical, statistical and survey projects carried out by RTI at the time of the Love Canal health crisis during the late 1970s. Probability sampling and chemical analysis of drinking water in 268 U.S. counties were included in research for the EPA after hazardous concentrations of the insecticide aldicarb were found in wells on Long Island, New York.

Corporations have also been among RTI's water quality research clients, most prominently and most recently the Monsanto Agricultural Company. To qualify one of the company's herbicides for EPA reregistration, the agency required Monsanto to obtain reliable estimates of the product's occurrence in the wells of rural counties. RTI designed a representative random sample of an estimated 6 million wells in a 26-state survey area. Monsanto and RTI reported to the EPA that approximately 87 percent of the sampled wells were free of any detectable level of the herbicide in question and four others, and that where their presence was detected it was in concentrations well below the EPA's health-based standard.

Camptothecin and a potential route to the marketplace for this unique antitumor compound illustrate a different kind of relationship between RTI and a corporate client, in this instance pharmaceutical giant Glaxo Inc., a Research Triangle Park neighbor. During 1989-90 negotiations, Glaxo obtained worldwide development and marketing rights to the camptothecin analogs patented by Wall and Wani and their colleagues. In return, Glaxo is to pay royalties to the Institute and provide supplementary funding for further research.

More good news issuing from camptothecin research and taxol's phase II clinical trials success is a revival of the National Cancer Institute's interest in natural products research. With NCI funding of several hundred thousand dollars per year, RTI has resumed its long-term effort of screening plant materials for anticancer activity.

As research for corporations and national defense agencies grew during the '80s, environmental and other health projects proliferated. One of the more notable has been, is, and will continue to be TEAM, the Total Exposure and Assessment Methodology studies. They represent the first use of statistically sampled populations to unravel the relationships between an individual's exposure to toxic substances and body burden, which is the amount of a specific chemical that's retained in body fluids and tissue. In trailblazing research that made TEAM possible, Pellizzari had, in the mid-70s, led a group of analytical chemists who became the first to find a means to simultaneously identify hundreds of volatile organic compounds (VOCs) in effluents and even in ambient air, where they can be found in traces measurable only in parts per trillion.

RTI's TEAM, which has included Harvard University and other subcontractors, trailblazed along several paths. One was in the development of wearable personal monitors that collect and concentrate the VOCs to which individuals are exposed daytimes, nighttimes, at work, at home, and during normal activities in between. Thanks to researchers' earlier demonstrations of innovative analytical methods, concentrations of VOCs—chloroform, benzene, toluene, and others—in a monitor's removable cartridge could be determined, and an individual's body burden established from biological samples, i.e., breath, urine, blood, nursing mothers' milk.

Among the dozens and dozens of TEAM's data collection and data analysis products, the most highly publicized have been findings related to indoor air pollution, a topic that was of no concern when the project started in the late 1970s. In Bayonne and Elizabeth, both in New Jersey and both, along with Greensboro, North Carolina, and Devil's Lake, North Dakota, among TEAM's prepilot and pilot study sites, air quality was monitored outside the homes of TEAM's statistically selected volunteers at the same time that the participants themselves wore vests with personal air monitors attached. For nearly every chemical of interest, the values recorded from the personal monitors were much higher than those from the fixed, outdoor monitors. The health implications were clear, for most Americans spend from 70 to 90 percent, or even more, of their time indoors where, even in unpolluted locales, they may breathe air that couldn't meet the EPA's clean air standards for out-of-doors. Airtight newer homes and office buildings were particularly suspect. Some of their energy-efficient characteristics lead to limited fresh air intake and, therefore, to slow-paced dilution of chemical emissions from such culprits as floor wax, new carpeting, fresh paint, cleaning solution residues, cigarette smoke. These emissions were responsible for "sick building syndrome," a complaint that afflicts thousands of people who breathe harmful indoor air.

During the 1980s RTI completed indoor air research projects with a contract value of more than $20 million. TEAM itself is a classic example of interdisciplinary research, involving RTI analytical chemists, chemical engineers, gas chromatograph/mass spectrometer analysts, biomedical engineers, and statistical, sampling, and survey specialists, plus researchers in these and other fields at the EPA and subcontracting organizations.

Indoor air as a health concern was only incidental to TEAM's original purposes, and its discovery as a hazard was almost accidental. It virtually backed into the public's health consciousness.

Meanwhile, three other health issues had arisen to confront the public more openly, and just as unexpectedly, and RTI responded to all three new national research priorities: radon, post-traumatic stress disorder, and AIDS.

Radon. Radon is "new" only by courtesy; after all, this radioactive gas—it occurs naturally from the breakdown of radium—has been around since the world's creation. The colorless, odorless gas was at one time a known contributor to high rates of lung cancer among uranium miners, but this threat vanished in the mid-1960s after the mines were equipped with adequate ventilation systems. It returned with a vengeance twenty years later. By 1985-86 radon was claiming headlines as a major health hazard, often listed as the second leading cause of lung cancer after cigarettes. Also by then, RTI had begun to carry out long-term radon research programs that involved sampling and survey statistics, geology, environmental quality assurance, and risk assessment.

Radium, radon's precursor, occurs in small amounts in most soils, and is concentrated in deposits of uranium, granite, shale, phosphate, and pitchblende. When these materials give off radon, a small portion of the gas escapes to the surface, where it usually dissipates harmlessly. It can, however, find its way into a building through cracks in the foundations, through sump pumps, floor drains, slab joints, and fittings around underground utility pipes. Once inside, radon continues its decay process, creating radon daughters, or progeny. If these progeny attach to dust, smoke, or other particles in the air, and are inhaled by a human, they can be trapped in the lungs and lead to cancer.

Homeowners the country over became concerned about possible radon contamination. One EPA estimate put the number of homes with potentially hazardous levels at 8 million. Together with the Surgeon General, the agency recommended radon testing for every house in the nation. Such an irresistible market brought forth a profusion of devices and services for radon detection. The EPA cannot endorse products, but through its National Radon Measurement Proficiency Program, coordinated by RTI's earth and mineral sciences department, it evaluates the various devices and mitigation services for the guidance of homeowners, builders, and state and local officials. Companies whose detectors measure radon with acceptable accuracy levels are included in lists published by the EPA. (The agency also publishes a homeowner's guide to radon reduction methods.) In 1986, the first year of the EPA/RTI measurement proficiency program, 39 companies submitted their products for testing. In 1989, to suggest the market's dimensions, the program evaluated the radon measurement services offered by several thousand firms.

PTSD. Post-traumatic stress disorder isn't new either, its symptoms going far back into human history, symptoms of emotional turmoil caused by the persistent, distressing, and uncontrollable reliving of some overwhelming experience such as combat, physical assault, accident, injury, or natural disaster. The prevalence of PTSD and other readjustment problems among American veterans of the war in Vietnam became an RTI project for the Veterans Administration, a four-year, nine-million-dollar epidemiologic study of unprecedented scope.

PTSD is a direct descendant of what was known as shell shock in the Great War and as combat fatigue in World War II. In 1980 it was included for the first time in the American Psychiatric Association's guide to mental disorders. In 1983 Congress mandated a comprehensive study to resolve the conflicting opinions it had heard for years about the mental health status and general life readjustment of Vietnam veterans. RTI won the contract and started work on it in September 1984.

The next four years produced what senior survey research methodologist Richard A. Kulka described as "perhaps the most far-reaching and ambitious national epidemiologic study ever attempted on any population." The tasks that RTI designed for the study were arduous at best. From military records on the approximately 8.2 million men and women who were in the armed forces during the ten-year Vietnam era, random samples were drawn from those who were on active duty in the war zones (Vietnam, Laos, Cambodia) and from those who were on active duty but not in a war zone. For further comparison, a third group was sampled, nonveterans, or civilian counterparts, people who weren't in the armed forces during the Vietnam era but who matched the theater veterans by age, sex, and race/ethnicity.

After identifying a survey sample of more than 3,000 individuals, RTI then had to mount a monumental tracking effort to find them. Ten to 15 or even 20 years after their military service ended, the individuals included in these subsets (a highly mobile population given to job changes, moving, dropping out) had to be traced, often through multiple addresses, located in 50 states and abroad, and then asked to give clinical interviews about their mental and other health status and about their general readjustment to civilian life. The interviews lasted an *average* of 3 to 5 hours, often probing deeply and painfully into emotional troubles and other highly personal readjustment problems that may have been caused by military service, especially by traumatic combat or other war-related events.

The broad conclusion, based on examination of more than 100 different adjustment indicators and contained in a December 1988 report to Congress, is that most Vietnam theater veterans made a successful reentry into civilian life. Nevertheless, while this "is true for the aggregate," as senior research psychologist William E. Schlenger reported at an RTI board meeting in May 1989, "we found that just over 15 percent of male Vietnam theater veterans, and almost 9 percent of women . . . have PTSD today, 15 to 20 years after their war experience. This represents about 480,000 veterans . . . an astounding number." *Trauma and the Vietnam War Generation*, a book published in 1990 by Brunner/Mazell, was written by co-principal investigators Kulka, Schlenger, John A. Fairbank, and B. Kathleen Jordan, all Ph.D. researchers at RTI, two University of California psychiatrists, and a Hispanic research specialist at San Diego State University.

AIDS. AIDS struck, apparently out of the blue, in mid-1981. Since then, efforts to combat the deadly epidemic have been America's most publicized public health concern and have been a dominating factor at RTI as well. In 1989, the peak year, so far, for AIDS research at the Institute, research related to the fatal disease accounted for $18.2 million in contract revenue, 20 percent of RTI's total.

Between 1979 and 1981, while the AIDS catastrophe was brewing, RTI's TOPS study of drug treatment outcomes was gathering information from and about intravenous drug users, a group that turned out to be at very high risk in the emerging AIDS epidemic. Sharing infected needles for intravenous drug use ranks second only to unsafe sexual practice as high risk behavior for AIDS, and it was a logical extension of TOPS to collect data on needle-sharing practices and to perform HIV blood tests on intravenous drug users. HIV is the human immunodeficiency virus that apparently causes AIDS.

RTI's greatest concentration of effort, $10.9 million in 1989 alone, was as clinical trials coordinating center for all AIDS-treatment trials that were funded over a five-year period, beginning in 1986, by the National Institute of Allergy and Infectious Diseases (NIAID). Thanks to biometrics vice president Poole, epidemiologic studies director Bryan, medical statistics research director Tyler D. Hartwell, and others in their centers, RTI already had years of extensive experience, and a reputation to match, in the collection, management, and analysis of data from large, multicenter clinical trials. But nothing in the history of medical research had approached what was to become the world's largest, most complex, and most urgent clinical trials program.

What began in 1986 as a set of small studies involving data collection from fewer than 10 clinics had within a year expanded to data of greater scope provided by more than 80 clinics. By the end of 1989, that number zoomed to 150. Management requirements for collecting and reporting mountains of data brought problems of an urgency and complexity that neither clinical nor statistical science had faced.

Of the many new methods and procedures created for monitoring the AIDS clinical trials, RTI's unique distributed data collection system is but one. Every day, employees at each of the 150 medical centers enter information about every AIDS patient into personal computers. Every night, when telephone rates are low, RTI's computer center dials the PCs and retrieves the stored data so the laborious processes of quality assurance and data analysis can begin.

Other long-term AIDS research, this for the National Cancer Institute, is on the epidemiology of retroviruses, of which HIV is but one, in the United States, the Caribbean, and Africa. These projects have been led from RTI's offices in Washington, D.C., and from an office in England. Work on AIDS prevention has focused on educational and other means for reducing needle-sharing among cocaine and heroin users, and on protecting sexually active adolescents. The lone chemistry and life sciences AIDS project to date involved synthesizing isotopically-labeled samples of pharmaceuticals being investigated as treatments for the virus.

Starting in 1990, RTI will provide clinical site monitoring for a broadened program of NIAID research on AIDS treatments.

Postscript

Events don't begin and end in neat, decade-long packages at RTI any more than they do anywhere else. So it's only coincidence that this narrative ends with RTI at the threshold to the 1990s, poised for accomplishments by the millennium that may astonish present readers as much as the first 31 years of accomplishment have astonished those who got it all started.

The purpose of the next few paragraphs is neither to predict nor to speculate upon what those accomplishments will be. It's enough to have assurance of their worth and their origin. Their worth can be expressed in a refrain whose words are never trite—contributions to scientific advance and the quality of life. Their origin was expressed by Horvitz when he stated that "At RTI, development of research concepts and the marketing of them are integrated functions. It is the responsibility of the senior scientific leadership of each program to create and market ideas. This marketing mode has nurtured a philosophy which contributes to RTI's success. In essence, each staff member has the opportunity to develop his or her own scientific interests and to market them. Projects are neither dictated nor assigned by top management."

This philosophy ranks high among the precedents, the standards, and the methods that mark RTI's way of doing business, what's come to be called, with a touch of good old ostentation, its corporate culture. The basic tenet that governs RTI operations makes a point similar to Horvitz's, but broader. Herbert put it that "Only people have ideas and conceive novel solutions for tough research problems. Only people put these ideas on paper and test them in the laboratory or model them with computers. In turn, these people are supported by scores of equally important people who print and bind reports, collect data, care for laboratory mice, move furniture into a new building, or maintain older buildings. These hardworking people are RTI."

A handful of supplementary institutional character traits further illuminate RTI's corporate culture, some with a sentence or two, a couple with a short paragraph.

— Much of RTI research is steeped in innovation and relatively little relies on routine. New methods, new techniques, new designs, new instruments, new systems are what make RTI and its clients happiest. Tasks that retrace steps already taken are less welcome. A case in point is YATS, the survey of young people's attitudes toward military service. A new research problem calling for new research approaches in the early 1980s, YATS was a welcome challenge to Institute social and statistical scientists, who were rewarded by the Department of Defense with several contract renewals. By decade's end the survey design was well established, survey operations were becoming routine, and the DoD hired a less expensive contractor while RTI went on to new challenges. Examples can be taken from any RTI research center.

— RTI isn't perfect and is up front about it. Asked about errors in a 1990 socioeconomic trend analysis, Cruze told news reporters that "We are embarrassed and dismayed that these mistakes were made. They are inexcusable errors."
— No matter how many rabbits financial vice president Bill Perkins pulls out of construction financing hats, RTI will never, probably never, have enough space on campus.
— Capital equipment budgets aren't ever likely to be lavish, but researchers can count on having the essentials. To maintain its hard-won reputation for excellence, RTI will strive to support staff capabilities in such already mentioned fields as survey research, computing, semiconductor design and fabrication, environmental measurements, and analytical chemistry, and also in some that haven't been included in this account such as waste treatment, particle physics, computer-aided drug design, and mammalian genetics.
— Project overruns will always be deplored. They are costly, reduce net income, inhibit management's ability to supply the essentials just mentioned, and serve clients poorly.
— Administrative and service functions will usually be understaffed. Research staff will never believe it.
— Research managers will always struggle with ITE, indirect technical expense. Decisions about allocating researchers' time between project work and program development—meaning professional advancement, proposal preparation, marketing—will remain difficult.
— Business office needs affect research operations, but never control them.
— Recruiting standards remain unchanged from the early days when Herbert went after the best he could find to be the Institute's initial research directors. RTI still wants and deserves the best scientists and engineers, and enjoys great success in bringing them aboard. Fortunately, most senior recruiting requirements are now filled from within. The Institute's senior executives' careers have brought them,

and RTI, national reputations in their fields. With only four exceptions, as of the end of 1989, the careers and reputations of the more than forty research vice presidents and center directors have been built at RTI. Staff scientists they have recruited will in most cases be their successors.

— As the Research Triangle area grows and fills up with newcomers, RTI's prominence will wane on the local scene even as it waxes nationally. The Institute of 1990 and beyond inevitably will be viewed as something that was always there. After all, 30 years have gone by since those lonesome days when the brave but tiny RTI was, along with Chemstrand, all there was in what several dozen university and civic leaders hoped might someday become a viable Research Triangle Park.

— Vital, enduring, and unique are but three of the adjectives that most readily describe RTI's ties with the founding schools. North Carolina State University, Duke University, and the University of North Carolina at Chapel Hill must always be recognized as the alpha and omega of the entire Research Triangle proposition.

— Hardworking people are RTI.

Acknowledgements

Members of RTI's Publication and Design staff were responsible for producing this book. Thank you.

For their valuable counsel on production aspects of the publication, RTI is grateful to Richard Hendel and Matthew Hodgson of the University of North Carolina Press, and to Lawrence J. Malley and Mary Mendell of the Duke University Press.

Appendix 1

RTI Corporate Organization, July 1991

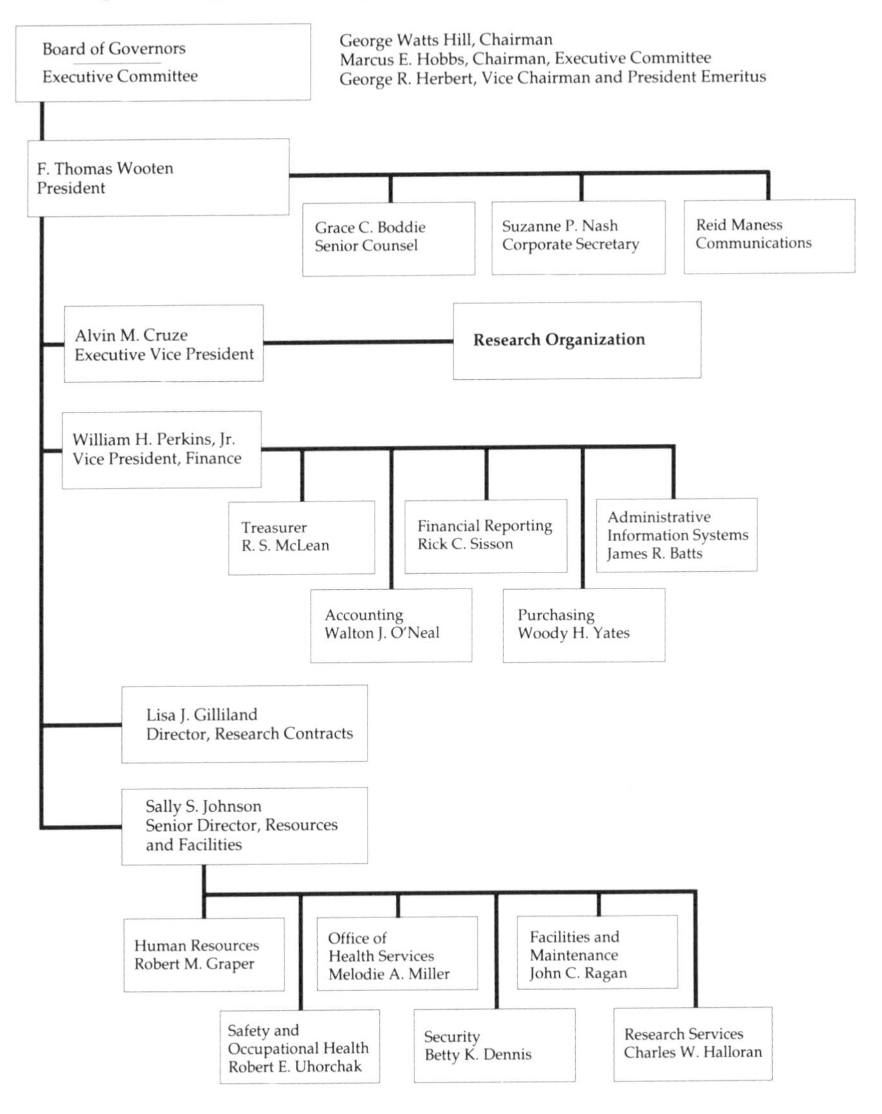

RTI Research Organization, July 1991

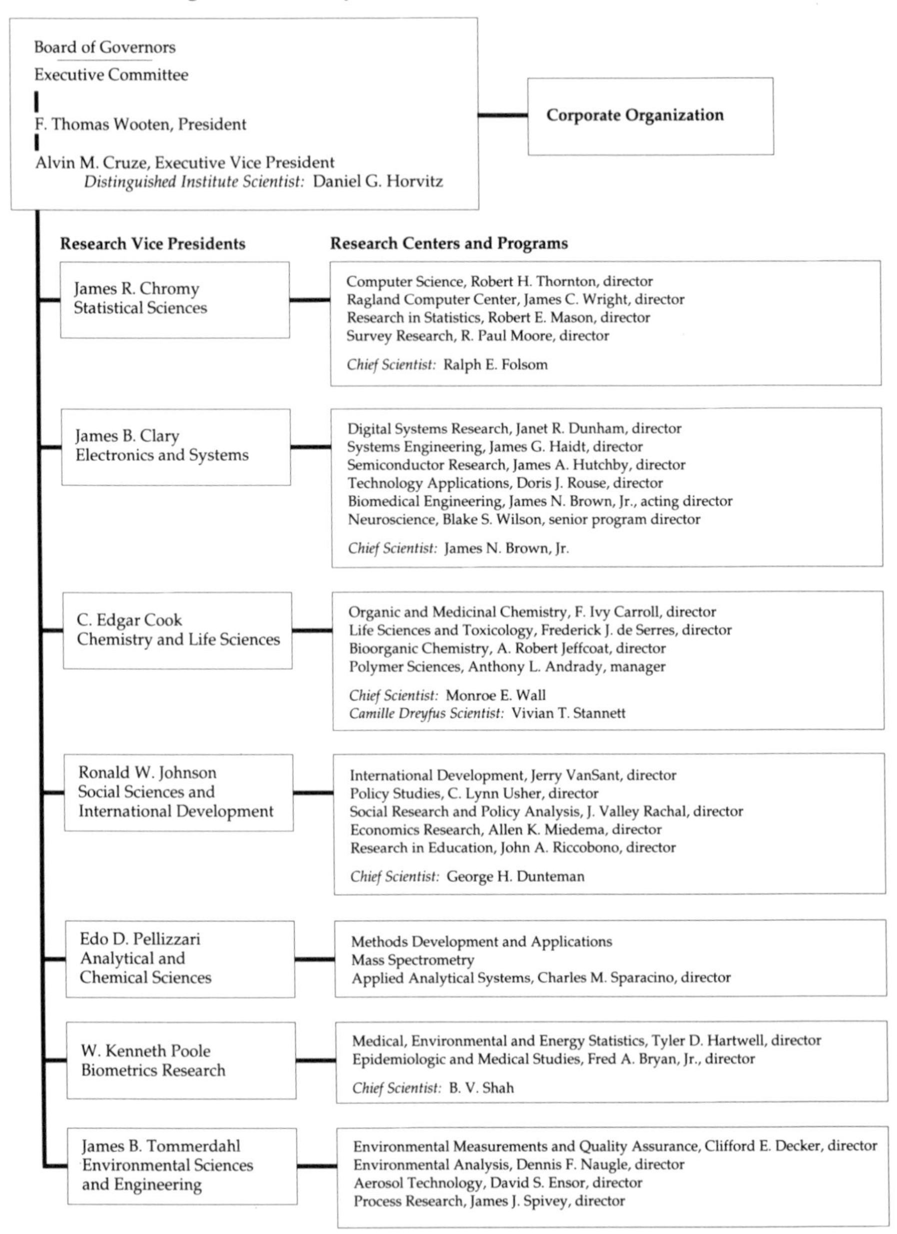

Appendix 2

Research Revenue

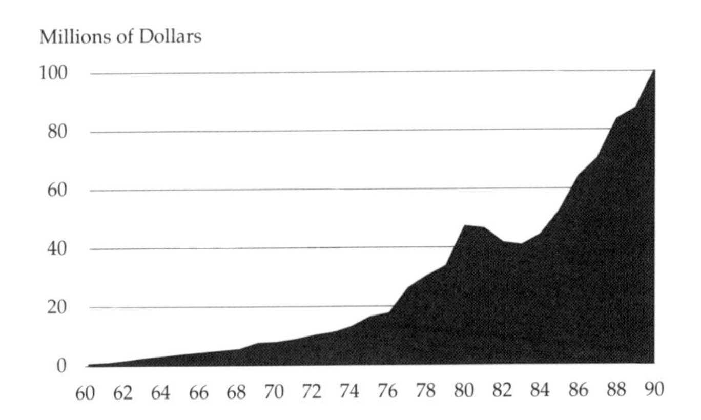

Staff Growth

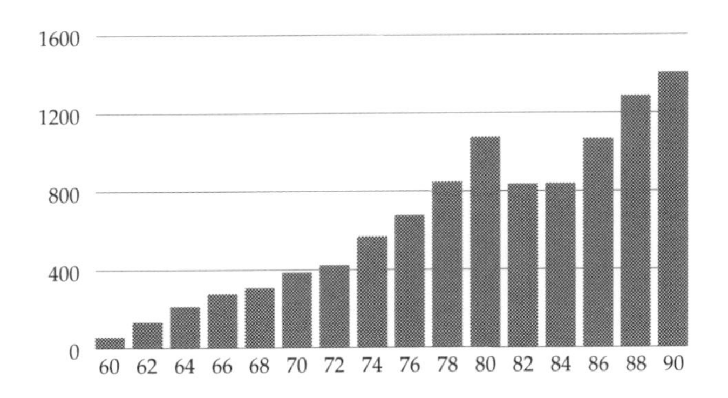

Appendix 3: Research Triangle Institute Board of Governors

December 1958 – July 1991

Five Governors hold seats by virtue of their positions: the presidents of The University of North Carolina, Duke University, and Research Triangle Institute, and the chancellors of North Carolina State University and the University of North Carolina at Chapel Hill.

Nine are appointed annually to represent Duke University, The University of North Carolina, N.C. State University, and UNC-Chapel Hill.

Up to 15 Governors are elected from the business and professional communities.

Additional individuals have been specified by name in the Bylaws.

A separate category of Lifetime Governor has recognized retired Board members who have made extraordinary contributions to the progress and welfare of RTI.

The following is an alphabetical list of all who have served on the RTI Board of Governors. Affiliations listed are as of the beginning of Board service and/or as of 1991. Those who have served as members of the Board's Executive Committee are identified by an asterisk.

Donald B. Anderson,* The University of North Carolina,
10/60-6/66 Appointed

Robert T. Armstrong,* Celanese Corp., NY, 1/59-11/74 Elected;
11/74- Lifetime

Norman R. Augustine, Martin Marietta Corp., MD, 9/83-11/87 Elected

William B. Aycock, UNC-Chapel Hill, 1/59-10/64 Appointed

John C. Bailar, III, McGill University School of Medicine,
Montreal, Canada, 11/89- Elected

William W. Bates, Jr., Liggett & Myers Inc., Durham, NC, 11/72-11/75 Elected

Donald S. Beilman, Microelectronics Center of North Carolina, RTP, NC, 11/80-6/88 Elected

William Bevan, Duke University, 11/79-11/82 Appointed

Erich Bloch, Council on Competitiveness, Washington, DC, 11/90- Elected

Carey H. Bostian, N.C. State University 1/59-8/59 Appointed

Garrett Briggs,* N.C. State University, 10/81-11/83 Appointed

H. Keith H. Brodie, Duke University, 11/82-6/85 Appointed; 6/85- By Position

John T. Caldwell, N.C. State University, 8/59-10/72 Appointed; 11/72-6/75 By Position

Harry C. Carter, J. P. Stevens & Co., Greensboro, NC, 1/59-11/65 Elected

Ivie L. Clayton,* Raleigh, NC, 11/79- Elected

Norman A. Cocke, Duke University, 12/58-1/59 (Incorporator)

Fred A. Coe, Jr., Burroughs Wellcome Co., RTP, NC, 11/71-11/81 Elected

R. Taylor Cole, Duke University, 11/60-11/69, Appointed

Pedro Cuatrecasas, Warner-Lambert Co., MI, 11/81- Elected

Linwood C. Dail, Duke Power Company, Charlotte, NC, 11/80-11/86 Elected

Frank A. Daniels,* The News and Observer Publishing Co., Raleigh, NC, 11/59-11/74 Elected; 11/74-5/86 Lifetime

Wilburt C. Davison, Duke University, 1/59-11/60 Appointed

Raymond H. Dawson,* The University of North Carolina, 11/68- Appointed

Charles A. Dewey, Jr., Duke Power Company, Charlotte, NC, 11/74-11/80 Elected

Fairleigh S. Dickinson, Jr., Becton Dickinson & Co., NJ, 11/72-11/81 Elected

Clyde A. Dillon, Dillon Supply Co., Raleigh, NC, 1/59-11/59 Elected

Earl G. Droessler,* N.C. State University, 11/73-7/7 Appointed

A. Hollis Edens, Duke University, 12/58-1/59 (Incorporator); 1/59-11/60 By Position

E. Y. Floyd, Plant Food Institute, Raleigh, NC, 1/59-11/62 Elected

Christopher C. Fordham, III, UNC-Chapel Hill, 5/80-6/88 By Position

William C. Friday, The University of North Carolina, 12/58-1/59 (Incorporator); 1/59-5/86 By Position; William R. Kenan Jr. Fund, Chapel Hill, NC, 5/86- Named in Bylaws

Leon Golberg, Chemical Industry Institute of Toxicology, RTP, NC, 11/77-11/80 Elected

Craufurd D. Goodwin, Duke University, 11/80-11/86 Appointed

Steve C. Griffith, Jr., Duke Power Company, Charlotte, NC, 11/87- , Elected

Phillip A. Griffiths,* Duke University, 11/84-6/91 Appointed

Paul M. Gross,* Duke University, 1/59-5/84 Appointed; 5/84-5/86 Named in Bylaws

Philip Handler, National Academy of Sciences, Washington, DC, 11/79-1/82 Elected

P. Huber Hanes, P. H. Hanes Knitting Co., Winston-Salem, NC, 1/59-11/65 Elected

Hiram R. Hanmer, American Tobacco Co., Durham, NC, 1/59-11/60 Elected

Paul Hardin, UNC-Chapel Hill, 7/88- By Position

Margaret T. Harper,* The Stephens Agency, Southport, NC, 11/74- Elected

Deryl Hart, Duke University, 11/60-11/63 By Position

Franklin D. Hart,* N.C. State University, 11/83- Appointed

C. E. Hartford, Riegel Paper Corp., Riegelwood, NC, 11/60-1/70 Elected

Charles E. Hayworth, Alma Desk Company High Point, NC, 11/65-11/77 Elected

Alexander Heard,* UNC-Chapel Hill, 1/59-1/63 Appointed

George R. Herbert,* Research Triangle Institute, 1/59-9/89 By Position; 10/89- Named in Bylaws

Grover M. Hermann, Martin-Marietta Corp., MD, 4/64-11/74 Elected; 11/74-11/79 Lifetime

George Watts Hill,* Central Carolina Bank & Trust Company, Durham, NC, 1/59-11/83 Elected (Chairman, 1959-); 11/83- Named in Bylaws

Marcus E. Hobbs,* Duke University, 1/59- Appointed (Chair, Executive Committee, 9/62-1/69, 9/70-1/71, & 12/77-)

Luther H. Hodges, Governor of North Carolina, 12/58-1/59 (Incorporator)

C. Hugh Holman,* UNC-Chapel Hill, 2/63-10/65 Appointed

William G. Howard, Jr., National Academy of Engineering, Washington, DC, 11/89- Elected

Charles B. Huestis, Duke University, 11/69-11/79 Appointed

Earl Johnson, Jr.,* Southern Industrial Constructors, Raleigh, NC, 11/73- Elected

Paul A. Johnston, Glen Alden Corp. NY, 11/65-11/72 Elected

Lyle V. Jones,* UNC-Chapel Hill, 11/72-10/79 Appointed

Frank H. Kenan, Kenan Oil Company, Chapel Hill, NC, 11/65-11/71 Elected

Huger King,* Richardson Corp., Greensboro, NC, 1/59-11/65 Elected

William L. Klarman,* N.C. State University, 9/90- Appointed

Douglas M. Knight, Duke University, 11/63-11/69 By Position

Matthew Kuhn, Microelectronics Center of North Carolina, RTP, NC, 9/87- Elected

William F. Little,* UNC-Chapel Hill, 11/65- Appointed
(Chair, Executive Committee 2/69-8/70 & 2/71-11/77)

G. Philip Manire,* UNC-Chapel Hill, 11/79-11/84, Appointed

J. Lee Marsh,* Union Carbide Chemicals Co., NY, 11/60-8/72 Elected

Eugene J. McDonald, Duke University, 11/90- Appointed

John C. McKinney, Duke University, 11/69-11/80 Appointed

Jasper Memory,* N.C. State University, 11/83-11/84 Appointed

A. C. Menius, Jr.,* N.C. State University, 11/72-11/73 Appointed;
7/79-10/81 Appointed

Leo J. Miller, Texas Gulf Sulphur Co., Aurora, NC, 11/65-11/66 Elected

Larry K. Monteith, N.C. State University, 11/84-10/89 Appointed;
10/89- By Position

Lloyd N. Morrisett, The John & Mary R. Markle Foundation, NY, 11/70-11/79 Elected

Walter M. Nielsen, Duke University, 1/59-11/60 Appointed

George E. Norman, Jr.,* Burlington Industries, Inc., Greensboro, NC, 11/72-10/90 Elected

J. Dennis O'Connor,* UNC-Chapel Hill, 11/88-7/91 Appointed

Jonathan W. Old, Jr., Liggett Group, Inc., Durham, NC, 11/75-11/79 Elected

Everett D. Palmatier,* UNC-Chapel Hill, 11/62-11/68 Appointed

Thomas J. Pearsall, Rocky Mount, NC, 11/66-11/73 Elected

R. James Peeler, Jr.,* N.C. State University, 9/74-9/75 Appointed

Walter J. Peterson,* N.C. State University, 1/59-9/74 Appointed; 11/74-11/80 Lifetime

Bruce R. Poulton, N.C. State University, 6/82-9/89 By Position

Charles E. Putman,* Duke University, 11/86- Appointed

Herbert T. Randall, Champion Papers, Inc., OH, 11/62-11/66 Elected

C. W. Reynolds,* Western Electric Co., Winston-Salem, NC, 1/59-11/62 Elected

William M. Riegel, Riegel Paper Co., Riegelwood, NC, 1/70-4/72 Elected

Jackson A. Rigney, N.C. State University, 7/75-12/75 By Position

Thomas A. Rose, Blue Cross & Blue Shield of NC, Durham, NC, 11/74- Elected

Terry Sanford, Cannon and Hunter, Raleigh, NC, 11/68-5/70 Elected; Duke University, 5/70-6/85 By Position; 11/85-11/86 Appointed

W. Bailey Sellars,* Burlington Industries, Raleigh, NC, 11/62-11/72 Elected; 11/74-1/79 Lifetime

Paul F. Sharp, UNC-Chapel Hill, 10/64-5/66 Appointed

George L. Simpson, Jr,* UNC-Chapel Hill, 1/59-8/62 Appointed (Chair, Executive Committee, 1/59-8/62)

J. Carlyle Sitterson, UNC-Chapel Hill, 5/66-11/72 Appointed

Patricia C. Skarulis, Duke University, 11/86-11/90 Appointed

C. D. Spangler, Jr., The University of North Carolina, 3/86- By Position

Vivian T. Stannett,* N.C. State University, 9/75-6/82 Appointed

Louis C. Stephens, Jr., Pilot Life Insurance Co., Greensboro, NC, 11/72-11/80 Elected

N. Ferebee Taylor, UNC-Chapel Hill, 11/72-6/80 By Position

Joab L. Thomas, N.C. State University, 1/76-6/81 By Position

Thomas J. Troup, Burr-Brown Corp., AZ, 11/81- Elected

C. M. Vanstory, Jr., North Carolina National Bank, Greensboro, NC, 11/66-11/68 Elected

Charles B. Wade, Jr., RJR Industries, Winston-Salem, NC, 11/80- Elected

J. M. Wasson,* Southern Bell Co., Charlotte, NC, 1/59-11/64 Elected

William S. Wells,* The University of North Carolina, 9/66-11/72 Appointed

Harold W. Whitcomb, Fieldcrest Mills, Eden, NC, 1/59-11/60 Elected

Albert N. Whiting,* North Carolina Central University, Durham, NC, 11/72-6/83 Elected

William M. Whyburn,* The University of North Carolina,
1/59-10/60 Appointed

Samuel R. Williamson, Jr.,* UNC-Chapel Hill, 11/84-7/88 Appointed

John B. Wilson,* Wright Machinery Co., Durham, NC, 1/59-11/62 Elected

Nash N. Winstead,* N.C. State University, 11/81-6/82 By Position;
6/82-11/83 Appointed; 11/89-9/90 Appointed

Barnes Woodhall, Duke University, 11/60-5/70 Appointed

F. Thomas Wooten,* Research Triangle Institute, 10/89- By Position

Phail Wynn, Jr., Durham Technical Community College, Durham, NC,
11/83- Elected

* Indicates service on the Executive Committee.

Index

D

E

F

G

R

S

T

U

V

W

Y

Z

Complimentary